DEATH OF A RACEHORSE

Cartwright looked in at Shoestring, who was standing with his rump close to the door, head down, asleep. Cartwright studied those fine quarters, and nodded as if to confirm everything he had told Jenkins about the horse.

A big bay, a promising hunter, was next to Shoestring, and next to the hunter was Silver Monarch. Cartwright approached this box with the kind of veneration felt by everyone associated with the horse; here was another Tulyar, another name to worship. He opened the top half of the door quietly, peering in and expecting to see the grey standing back to him, still in sleep.

He saw the horse on its side, and was so astonished that he stood gaping.

Then he heard a movement at the side of the box, and as he glanced round, saw a man with his right arm raised, and a weapon in his hand.

"No!" he gasped. "No——"

The man struck savagely at his head.

Death of a Racehorse

John Creasey

CORONET BOOKS
Hodder Paperbacks Ltd., London

Copyright © 1959 by the Executors of
John Creasey Deceased
First published by Hodder and Stoughton 1959
Coronet edition 1962
Second impression 1975

/

Printed and bound in Great Britain for
Coronet Books,
Hodder Paperbacks Ltd,
St. Paul's House, Warwick Lane,
London, EC4P 4AH
by Hazell Watson & Viney Ltd,
Aylesbury, Bucks

ISBN 0 340 19477 4

CONTENTS

CHAPTER I

THE THREAT

'I'LL KILL that horse,' Lady Foley said, quite loudly. 'It will be Lionel's ruination.'

The guests near her, hearing the world 'kill' uttered with a viciousness which could not be mistaken, fell silent. This silence reached out and lay upon the others in the room, so that each one of the twenty-three people present heard the words 'Lionel's ruination'.

Lionel Foley was standing with his back to his mother, some yards away, a tray with several empty and one full sherry glass in his hand. He stopped smiling, but did not turn round. The Gales, at one of the rare cocktail parties at Foley Hall, saw how his lips tightened and his eyes narrowed, and sensed his sudden gust of anger.

Even then, the awkwardness might have been smoothed over had Colonel Madden not been present. The Colonel had racing in his blood, horses and betting were his life, a somewhat precarious life. It was customary for him to take an opposite view to his sister's, whatever the subject.

'Nonsense, Martha,' he said clearly. 'The horse will be the making of him.'

Near the great log fire, where it was much too hot, a neighbour who liked all the family spoke in a too-loud voice to three elderly women who were near the hearth.

'In spite of this cold snap, I think we're going to have a mild winter. Hedgehogs simply don't hibernate close to the ground unless we are, and in my garden there are three so near the surface that . . .'

Over at the grand piano, which told today's world how the Foleys of the past had lived, young Jane Madden began to strum a popular tune, talking clearly above it:

'That's exactly how it goes. If you can explain how that ever got into the top twenty, I'll be everlastingly grateful. What it wants is a bit of the Blues. I'm sick to death of skiffle and rock and – now, listen, and see what I mean.'

She began to play loudly and clearly, and the saxophones and drums seemed to be in the background, eager to take part. She swayed a little and rolled her eyes, and the rhythm took on an almost primeval fascination. The younger members of the party, including the Gales, looked towards her, and several of them moved towards the piano.

'When Jane gets a Blues mood on her there's no stopping her,' said Lionel, outwardly calm. 'Do you go for it?'

'I love it,' John Gale said, too fervently.

'I can never keep still,' declared Daphne Gale, and began to wriggle her slim shoulder, to widen her startlingly blue eyes and look like a clockwork doll; no one ever believed that Daphne was real.

'We'll have a jam session one of these days,' said Lionel. The colour was back in his cheeks, and he had recovered remarkably quickly. 'Have you met Mr and Mrs Clay-thorpe? They must be among your nearest neighbours . . .'

So it was all glossed over, but in spite of Jane and her Blues and in spite of everyone's determined efforts, the atmosphere did not really thaw. By seven o'clock the first guests were on the way out, and by a quarter past the Gales left, thanking hostess and young host with a little too much warmth. They went to their car, which was parked at the head of the long drive through Foley Park. The moon was up, and it was a clear, bright night; already frost was spark-ling on the November-bared branches of the nearer trees, and on the grass immediately outside the lighted window. By night when the front of the house was occupied, it was possible to imagine that the Foleys were back in their heyday, to believe that coaches would soon come round from the stables where the grooms had been entertained, the clip-clop-clip-clop of horses' hoofs would be sharp and clear, link boys would spring forward with torches blazing. Instead, just one car was left, the Gales' medium sized Austin.

Madden's daughter Jane, the pianist peacemaker, came out and straddled her motor-scooter.

'That's one party I wish I hadn't come from London for,' she said. 'I'm off to Corsica tomorrow though. Sun and skiffle. Goodbye!'

'Goodbye,' John echoed, hardly noticing what she said.

'Have a good time,' called Daphne, and the girl's machine went pop-popping down the drive. Gale helped Daphne into the Austin and then took the wheel, adjusting his coat over his knees.

'You warm enough, sweet?'

'I'm warmer out here, anyhow.'

'Don't be beastly to the Foleys.'

'Darling,' said Daphne, as John pulled the self-starter and the engine purred, 'Lady Foley meant exactly what she said: she will kill Shoestring if she ever gets a chance.'

'Nonsense.' They were moving down the private road, and the headlights made surprisingly little impression on the moonlight. 'Something happened to annoy her, that's all. We've always known that she wasn't normal on the subject of horses.'

'That's exactly what I mean. Did you see her face?'

'I saw Lionel's.'

'I saw both,' said Daphne. She stared straight ahead of her. The great watch tower known to everyone nearby as Foley's Folly loomed tall and dark, but they hardly noticed it, until they reached the end of the drive, half a mile from the house. Here they turned left, towards Arncott. Their home and the Arncott stables were on the edges of the old town, with the village of Foley four miles away – to the right of the drive from here.

'She looked as if she wished she could kill the horse then,' Daphne went on, 'and Lionel looked as if he could kill her.'

'Darling, you wouldn't let that fiery imagination of yours take hold of you, would you?'

'That wasn't imagination. John,' went on Daphne in a voice which her husband knew betrayed intense seriousness, 'I don't think you ought to train Shoestring for Lionel.'

'Now don't be absurd, sweet.'

'You don't want to become involved in the Foleys' family quarrels,' Daphne said quite sharply. 'Have you actually promised to train the horse?'

'Yes.'

'Can't you change your mind?'

'I suppose I could, but I don't want to,' Gale answered. 'It's a damned good horse. I expect it to win the Hampton Plate and probably the Amblon Cup in the spring and if it can put those in the bag it will go places.'

'It won't go anywhere if she kills it,' Daphne said tartly, 'and I'd rather it was killed in her stables than in ours.'

'You're making far too much of the thing,' Gale said. 'Forget the whole business, sweet.'

'Well,' retorted Daphne, still sharply, 'don't say I didn't warn you.'

John chuckled, and took a hand off the wheel long enough to press her knee.

'Don't start trying to make up to me,' Daphne said. 'You've made a lot of mistakes that you wouldn't have if you'd listened to me. Lady Foley's remark wasn't something that could be laughed off. I'll bet they're going at each other hammer-and-tongs now that they're alone.'

'They probably don't remember anything about it,' her husband argued. 'Forget it.'

*　　　*　　　*

Two miles away, in the drawing-room deserted now except for Lady Foley, Lionel and Colonel Madden, Lionel was standing by the piano, one arm resting on it, the flickering firelight shining on his pale face and making his eyes glitter.

There was a film of sweat on his forehead and upper lip, not wholly due to the warmth of the room. He was twenty-four, but at times looked years younger, for he was tall and slender, willowy and a little round-shouldered. He had fine grey eyes and a long, lean face, with bow-shaped lips which were almost feminine when relaxed; just now they were in a thin line.

'Now listen, you two,' the Colonel blustered into a tense pause, 'it's no use behaving as if the world's come to an end. Got to reconcile your differences, that's it and all about it. Lionel, you—'

'I say that it was absolutely unforgiveable,' Lionel said, 'and I'll never forgive you, Mother. Our differences have been bad enough when kept in the family, but to burst out like that when so many people were in the room, and John Gale—' He stopped, as if he couldn't express himself clearly; when he went on, he was almost inaudible. 'It'll be all over the place by the morning. I wouldn't be at all surprised to find it in the gossip columns. You must have been out of your mind.'

'Don't talk to your mother like that, Lionel.' The Colonel still tried to assert authority. 'What you need is a good stiff whisky.'

'I have never been more sane in my life,' declared Lady Foley, thin-voiced. 'Sooner or later Lionel had to be made to realize that I was serious, and tonight was as good a time as ever. No, don't interrupt me!' She raised her right hand, palm outwards, looking surprisingly impressive for a small woman. At fifty-nine, she had kept her figure remarkably well. Her royal blue dress suited her and picked out the blue in her eyes, the make-up was discreet and yet sufficient; she could easily be mistaken for fifty. Her hair was a light brown, and she had it rinsed just enough to keep the grey from becoming too obvious. The only likeness between her and her son was in the long nose and the square chin – which looked un-expected on each of them. 'I saw your father ruin himself and ruin me *and* you, because of horses. I had to stand by while he sold farm after farm, picture after picture, everything he had, simply to keep his horses running. It became such an obsession that it drove him mad, and to my dying day I shall believe that it killed him. I am not going to stand by and see you ruined by the same madness.'

There was a moment of silence, before Lionel stood up from the piano, stared at her, moistened his lips, and muttered in a high-pitched voice:

'Don't touch that horse. Understand? Don't touch that horse.'

He turned and went out of the room, into the spacious hall with its panelled walls on which great paintings had once hung; only three were left, none by a major artist, and all of the family. He went straight to the front door and let himself out, ignoring the sharpness of the cold after the heat of the room. He closed the door behind him loudly, and went hurrying down the four stone steps to the drive and then turned round towards the right, and the stables. He reached them, gasping for breath, not because he had hurried but because he was almost beside himself. A dim light burned at the gateway, another over the loosebox where he kept Shoestring. He heard the horse moving about in the box, clenched his teeth and tried not to give way to his feelings. He reached the box, and the horse's head appeared, nuzzling him. He fondled it, fighting back stinging tears of anger and vexation.

He went inside, switched on the light, and picked up a dandy-brush; the horse was groomed as well as it could be, but he could not bring himself to go back into the house, and had to do something. He began to brush the grey sides and flanks, and as he did so, heard someone approaching. He did not look round when his uncle appeared at the box entrance.

'Lionel, I want a word with you.'

'It won't be any good,' Lionel said. 'You know what she's like, and she means it. But if she ever touches Shoestring, I—'

'Don't say it!' the Colonel rasped. 'You don't know what

you're saying.' He opened the door of the box and came in. 'Good God, boy, don't you think I know how you feel? and don't you think I can't understand what's happening to your mother? She hates horses as much as you and I love them, and there's nothing you'll ever be able to do about it. She's right, too. They ruined your father and they've ruined me. Do you think I like living in a cottage on the estate? Do you think I like my own daughter going off as a governess to a couple of spoiled brats? I'm old enough now to know that I've brought all this on myself through love of horses. If you want my advice, you'll sell Shoestring, and get away from the Hall on the proceeds. Live your own life.'

'Sell——' Lionel began, and seemed to choke.

'It's the obvious thing to do. I think Gale would buy him, or at least find a buyer.'

'In two years' time Shoestring will have made a fortune for me!'

'If you knew how often your mother heard those words from your father you'd understand better how she feels,' the Colonel said, his voice much less harsh. 'Don't make too much of one horse, Lionel. I know you've had this one since it was a foal, I know you've doted on it, I know you think it's a world-beater, but probably all Shoestring will do is to run to a place now and again in a few minor handicaps. That's the law of averages. Don't I know it! Every man who loves horses believes he's found a world-beater sooner or later, but it only happens once every four or five years, and you're not likely to be a lucky one. Sell him, Lionel. Then you'll make quite sure that your mother isn't driven into doing anything that would really come between you, and you'll be able to keep going on your own for a while. If it wasn't so near here I'd suggest that you got a job with John Gale. He was telling me the other day that it's more and more difficult to find stable lads who work because they love horses as you do, my boy. Do the sensible thing, and cash in while you can, otherwise you'll come here one morning and find that your mother *has* poisoned Shoestring. Can't let that happen, it would be ludicrous.'

'I'll make sure that can't happen,' Lionel said bitterly. 'I'll take him down to the Gales' stable here and now, they'll stake him for a month or two if necessary.'

'I think John Gale would give you two thousand cash down,' the Colonel guessed.

'I'm not selling Shoestring, can't you get that into your head?' Lionel strode towards a saddle hanging on the wall, and lifted it down. 'I'll make a fortune out of that horse. You don't seem to understand, he's got everything.' He slung the saddle over Shoestring's back, and the horse reared a little under the unusually heavy thump. 'Steady, old boy,' he soothed, 'we'll soon be out of here.' He adjusted the saddle and began to tighten the girths, while the Colonel watched impotently.

CHAPTER II

DEATH OF A HORSE

KATHLEEN RUSSELL sat on the pouffe in front of a fire which blazed quite as brightly as that at Foley Hall, looked up at her sister, hugged her knees, and said:

'My money's on John.'

'It would be,' remarked Daphne, but the tartness was out of her voice. She still had the china-look, although she was curled up in an armchair on the other side of the fire. Kathleen was two years younger, but taller and larger, although not by any means a big woman. They were obviously sisters, their faces were flushed with heat, they had the easy naturalness of manner which had first attracted John Gale to Daphne, in whom it was so unexpected. Gale was sitting well back from the fire, brandy glass by his side, tweed-clad legs crossed at the ankles.

'My money's on Shoestring,' he observed.

'Pet, that's where you'll have us if you're not careful, on a shoestring,' Daphne said. 'We're not far off it now. If you lost a thousand pounds this year, we'd be broke, wouldn't we?'

'We'd get by.'

'Seriously, we haven't enough capital, and you've always admitted it. You know perfectly well that if you take on Shoestring for Lionel Foley, he won't be able to pay you, it'll be months before the horse is ready to race, and if he won one, how much profit would there be? A few hundred pounds, shared between you and the owner.'

'We've been married seven years and you haven't gone without bed and board yet,' Gale reminded her. 'And the horse isn't due here until after Christmas, so Christmas dinner should be all right.'

'In this mood, you're insufferable,' Daphne said. 'Oh, I

expect Kath's right, and you'll have your own way. But—'
Kathleen and Gale chanted:

'. . . *don't say that I didn't warn you.*'

They were still laughing when there was a ring at the front
door bell, and almost immediately a maid went to open it.
They heard voices, for the narrow hall led straight into this
study-cum-dining-room. One voice was a man's. Soon the
door opened, and the middle-aged maid announced:

'It's Mr Lionel Foley.'

Daphne threw up her arms in a kind of token of surrender
and dismay, and uncurled herself. Kathleen jumped up from
the pouffe and smoothed down her skirt. She took a quick
glance at a mirror over the mantelpiece, and ran her fingers
over her cheeks and nose, as if to get rid of a little of the
shine, while Gale went to the door.

'Hallo, Lionel. Come in.'

'Hope this isn't an infernal nerve,' Lionel said, 'but I
would like a talk with you if you can spare five minutes.' He
followed Gale into the room, saw Daphne, and then saw
Kathleen. He stared at her and bowed slightly. 'Good evening.'

'Hallo, Mr Foley,' Daphne said. 'I don't think you know
my sister Kathleen, do you?'

'No . . .' He hesitated, smiled and bowed slightly again.
'How are you?' He looked at Kathleen more intently, as if
she had momentarily taken his mind off his problem; but
that impression did not last for long, and he glanced round at
Gale.

'What will you have to drink?' Gale asked.

'Er – whisky and soda, thanks,' Lionel answered, and then
burst out: 'I've got Shoestring outside. I wonder if I could
take him round to the stables? That's if you've a box
empty—' He broke off, awkward to the point of gaucheness,
and glanced at Daphne as if he sensed the fact that she was
antagonistic. She looked surprised, Kathleen seemed to be
smothering a smile, and John Gale took the request with
commendable calm.

'Yes, of course.'

'I'm leaving for London for a week or two, unexpectedly,' Lionel explained, 'and there's no one at the house to look after him. Would it be a good idea if I took him round to the stables first?'

'I'll come with you,' Gale offered.

He winked at Daphne and her sister as they went out by a side door. Daphne grimaced at him. Kathleen was looking at Lionel Foley's back, but as the door closed, she said:

'Well, he certainly knows what he wants.'

'I've the uneasiest feeling that John's influenced because Lionel's an Honourable,' Daphne said, moving to a cocktail cabinet. 'Now I need a drink. The truth is that John thinks the Foley name still means something good in the racing world, whereas in fact it means failure. Oh, well, I suppose it will work out all right. At the worst it will cost us feed and lodging for one horse.'

'*Is* the horse any good?' asked Kathleen, opening her handbag and beginning to powder.

'I'm not sure whether John really thinks so or whether he wants to think so, but I believe it looks all right. I never really know – the best-looking horses always seem to finish last. That's plenty of make-up, darling, he's only an impoverished aristocrat with a spiteful mother and a big house which is so heavily mortgaged that he can't raise another penny on it. And Colonel Madden's just as badly off. He lives in a gardener's cottage because he and his sister get on each other's nerves.'

'That seems a bit silly,' Kathleen observed, obviously without much thought.

Daphne smiled, so sweetly.

'As a matter of fact since his wife died the Colonel's taken to having girl-friends who stay the night. Lady Foley wouldn't stand for that in the house, and he went to the cottage. He drove his daughter away from Foley Hall, too. She hated the sordidness of it.'

'And I rather liked the Colonel when I met him,' Kathleen said sorrowfully.

'Oh, you'll *like* him. John says that he's a kind of newshound for racing stables gossip, and scrapes a living that way because people do like him. It's all rather tragic, and tough on Lionel.'

'I felt sorry for him, he seemed so helpless,' Kathleen said.

'That's what I'm afraid of,' commented Daphne. 'Well I'd better put the best face I can on it, and be civil to him, anyhow. I suppose we'd better ask him to stay to dinner, although he almost certainly won't.'

'What's the betting?' asked Kathleen.

When the men returned, ten minutes later, Lionel looked less harassed, and John said bluffly:

'Have Doris lay another place for dinner, sweet, will you? I've asked Lionel if he can stay.'

*   *   *

'You don't suppose that her ladyship would do anything while the horse is here, do you?' asked Daphne, when she was sitting up in bed applying cold cream, and Gale was tying the sash of his blue and white striped pyjamas.

'You've got that on the brain,' he replied. 'Of course she won't. In any case, she can't. While we've got Silver Monarch here two lads are on night duty at the stables, and they'd know even if a dog came in when it shouldn't.'

'I hope you're right,' said Daphne.

'I think I have a recommendation to make, so that we can take your mind off such unromantic things as spiteful and possessive mothers and disappointed young men,' said Gale. 'Here I come!' He jumped into bed, took the cold cream jar from her hand and tossed it into an armchair. 'Now, little wifey, it's time that—'

'For goodness sake remember that Kath's in the next room!'

'Yes, dear,' said Gale, with mock meekness. 'Incidentally,

she was making large eyes at Lionel Foley over the dinner table, wasn't she?'

'Nonsense,' Daphne said. 'If I thought there was any risk of that, I'd send her packing tomorrow. It isn't that I don't like Lionel Foley, but he'll never have a penny to bless himself with. Who *is* on duty tonight?'

'This week the Cartwrights,' Gale told her. 'And you,' he added wickedly.

*   *   *

John Gale was at the stables, a little after six o'clock next morning, talking to Jenkins, his head lad, and to old Ted Cartwright, who was just going off duty. Other lads were leading their charges round the yard, horses were jerking their heads up and down, and looked bright in the crisp morning air. Cartwright, an elderly, wizened man, reported a quiet night, and went off.

'What time do you want them galloped this morning?' Jenkins asked. He was tall for an ex-jockey, and stood higher than Gale's shoulder, but he was painfully thin and his face looked as if it were carved out of wood browned by centuries in the open air.

'Half past seven, as usual,' Gale said. 'Have you had a look at the new recruit?'

'Yes,' said Jenkins, straight-faced.

Gale grinned. 'Don't you like him?'

'I didn't think I'd ever be helping to train a Foley horse again,' Jenkins said. 'Lord Foley was the worst judge of a racehorse I ever knew in my life; it was a tragedy he didn't realize it. But I suppose you had to take the colt in, in view of what was said last night.'

Gale frowned. 'About what?'

'About her ladyship's wild talk. Capable of doing it, too,' Jenkins added.

'Has that spread round already?' Gale sounded incredulous.

'It was going the rounds at the Foley Arms last night when

I was there just after nine,' said Jenkins. 'The Foleys are still news in this part of the world, Mr Gale. As for the horse—' he hesitated.

'Let's have it,' Gale said. 'I think he's the makings of a winner.'

'Never seen a horse with a bold eye like that which wasn't a winner,' Jenkins agreed. 'Handled well, that horse will make something all right.'

'Nice to know I can still see beyond the edge of my nose,' said Gale. 'How's Silver Monarch this morning?'

Jenkins had the kind of face which seemed never likely to soften, but it softened then, and his brown eyes kindled as he studied the grey at the head of the string.

'If Monarch doesn't take the Derby next year, I've never trained a horse,' he declared. 'That's going to make your name, Mr Gale, I never had any doubt of that. He's a fine horse and Mr Corrison's a good owner. I think it's going to be the start of a first-class team.'

'Sam, you've made my morning.'

'Glad I've made something, sir. Going to watch the gallop?' Jenkins asked.

'Yes, and I expect Miss Russell will be with us,' said Gale. 'If you really want to find out how much she knows about horses, ask her to tell Silver Monarch and Shoestring apart when you're on the heath.'

Jenkins' face cracked into a grin.

*   *   *

'I wouldn't be able to tell the difference even if they weren't of the same colour,' Kathleen said, 'but I like the smaller one best.'

'That's Silver Monarch,' Jenkins told her. 'Best two-year-old I've ever seen, Miss Kathleen, you can put your money on him for the Triple Crown. He won't let you down. Guard him like uranium, we do – he's nearly as valuable.'

*   *   *

The two 'lads' on night duty at the stables were used to being on call at any hour. One was an elderly man, Ted Cartwright, and the other a lad in every sense, Ted's sixteen-year-old son, Syd. Syd was taller than his father by half an inch; if they had a worry, it was that the son would not be able to restrict his rate of growth sufficiently to make the grade as a jockey; father and son had the same ambition.

Neither of them seriously thought that there was the slightest danger to Silver Monarch.

No one did, seriously. The night watch was a precaution which seemed excessive to some, but at the Arncott Stables there was such passionate belief in the future of Silver Monarch that no one had suggested that the caution was excessive. Cartwright was in charge of the horse, for his son had general duties by day. On this, the second night that Shoestring had been Silver Monarch's stable companion, father and son were in the small shed from which they could see the whole of the yard. A camp-bed stood in each of two corners, so that each lad could take his spell of sleep, and there were comfortable armchairs. It was a little after ten o'clock; neither of them had bedded down yet. A radio played softly from the corner of the shed, Syd Cartwright was reading a book, his father was reading the newspapers with the help of a magnifying glass; nothing would persuade him to have glasses. They were some distance from the main road, and only now and again did they hear the slightest sound; then it was a car, flashing by. No noise came from the house itself, because the Gales lived at the front, and the yard was at the back. Beyond them stretched Foley Heath, where horses from this stable had been exercised for over a hundred years.

The radio music was a calypso, gay but repeated over and over again until it lost all significance. The newspaper rustled whenever Ted Cartwright leaned further forward. He glanced at his watch, and saw that it was ten-fifteen. Without a word, he put down his newspaper, looked at his son, and went to the door.

Syd looked round.

'It's all right, Dad, I'll do this round. Why don't you be patient a minute?'

'Every half an hour, at the quarter past and the quarter to, that's the schedule,' his father said. 'If you work by the clock, Syd, you won't go far wrong. I'll go round now and then turn in.'

'Okay, Dad, if that's how you want it,' the boy said.

Cartwright went outside. Two electric lamps were spreading a dim light, one of them from the front of this shed, another from the gates, which were closed. A horse moved in a box, and then fell silent. Cartwright took a torch from his pocket, but he did not need to flash it on. The wide path which ran right round the stable yard was soft underfoot. In the middle was a circular lawn, with beautifully-tended flower beds; Jenkins' pride. In the distance the glow of a car's head-lamps showed in the sky; there was a hum of the car's engine, and then silence and darkness. The moon had set half an hour ago, and the stars looked pale and dim.

Cartwright approached the main gates.

In these was a small door, used by the lads as they came in and out when the main gates were closed. These gates were locked, chained and barred; the small door had a Yale lock, and was secured by a bolt top and bottom. Cartwright switched on his torch for the first time, doing the job thoroughly, although it did not occur to him that there was the slightest danger.

He noticed that the top bolt was not shot home, glanced down and saw that the bottom one was back, too. Astonished, he looked over his shoulder, but saw nothing unusual or suspicious. He stared at the closed door of the hut, frowning. Syd had been round here last, and should have made sure about the bolts; anyone who came in later than nine-thirty had to ring the bell.

Cartwright could have gone straight across to reprove his son, or could continue his rounds. He decided to continue the rounds, shot the bolts, and walked on. When he reached the first box, there was tension in his manner; but the horse, a yearling filly, was all right. So was a big plater in the next one. Cartwright glanced round at the gates again, as if to make sure that he had really found the door unbolted. There was no sound anywhere, not even from the big house, about fifty yards away.

Cartwright looked in at Shoestring, who was standing with his rump close to the door, head down, asleep. Cartwright studied those fine quarters, and nodded as if to confirm everything he had told Jenkins about the horse.

A big bay, a promising hunter, was next to Shoestring, and next to the hunter was Silver Monarch. Cartwright approached this box with the kind of veneration felt by everyone associated with the horse; here was another Tulyar, another name to worship. He opened the top half of the door quietly, peering in and expecting to see the grey standing back to him, still in sleep.

He saw the horse on its side, and was so astonished that he stood gaping.

Then he heard a movement at the side of the box, and as he glanced round, saw a man with his right arm raised, and a weapon in his hand.

'No!' he gasped. 'No—'

The man struck savagely at his head.

CHAPTER III

DEATH OF A MAN

OLD CARTWRIGHT felt the force and the agonizing pain of the blow, and could not call out. He fell against the outside of the door, but was still conscious, and tried to save himself. Once on the ground, he wanted to struggle to his feet, but there was such pain at his head and in his chest that he could not. He tried to cry out, but there was only a croaking sound. He felt the door open, and saw a man appear; he knew it was a man, because of the big foot, the big leg, in flannel trousering. He squinted upwards, but all he could see was a shadowy figure, looming over him and blotting out what light there was.

He gasped again: 'No, no!' Then great fear rose in him, for he knew what the man was going to do. He tried to cover his bare head with his arms, but was too late; a blow smashed upon his head, another and another.

With the fourth blow, he lost consciousness . . .

The man who had struck him stood over him, hesitating, staring at the hut where the light was over the door. The door remained tightly closed. He bent over the small figure of old Cartwright, and dragged him by his feet into Silver Monarch's box. He let him fall in a corner, then heaped hay over him, so that he was completely hidden. There was a slight trail of blood, and he picked up a fork and pushed hay about to cover this. All the time, he was breathing very heavily; and all the time the horse lay still, on its side.

The killer went out.

He stared across at the shed again; and the door was still closed. He shut the two halves of this door, then stepped over the bricks which led to the boxes and on to the soft track where the horses were exercised; on this he made no sound at all. He went swiftly towards the gate, and saw that the bolts had been shot. He muttered under his breath as he pulled these back. One of them squeaked, and he looked over his shoulder again, as the door of the Night Shed opened. Light streamed out, and the killer saw the shadow of a boy appear in front of it, long and misshapen. From the shed the man could not be seen so well as he could see, but he stood with one bolt drawn and the other still shot, knowing that the boy, who came further forward, was glancing about him.

He looked this way.

The boy called: 'Is that you, Dad?'

The killer drew the bolt back, cautiously; it was very tight. He did not move, apart from his right hand and arm, and he watched the boy all the time.

'Dad!'

The bolt slid back, and the killer opened the small door and stepped outside. As he did so, he heard the boy cry out:

'*Stop there!*'

The killer slammed the door and rushed towards the other side of the road, where a car was waiting, its engine ticking over. The driver leaned out and opened the door.

'Stop there!' came the boy's voice, much nearer now, and any moment the door might open.

'He see you?' the driver asked urgently.

'Too far away – get going.'

'Sure?'

'*Get going.*'

The car began to move forward as the killer leaned back in a corner, looking out of the rear window. The light was poor, but he saw the door open. The boy appeared for a moment, a silhouette against the misty light which came from the yard. Then the car shot past the house where the Gales lived, sped through the village, and across the downs.

*   *   *

Syd Cartwright stared at the disappearing red light and a dark shape in the night. He heard the hum of the noisy engine, but he did not think of the significance of that. He hesitated, feeling cold and very much alone, and then turned and looked about the deserted yard.

He raised his voice: 'Dad!'

There was no answer.

He began to walk swiftly towards the nearest box, and as he did so, looked at the light in the window of the flat, above the livery room, where Jenkins and his wife lived; it was surprising that the head lad had not heard him. He could go across to the Jenkins' flat right away; or he could ring the general alarm bell.

He was not yet sure that there was real cause for alarm, and felt that he ought to find out. He ran first towards Silver Monarch's box, knowing that if anything had gone wrong he was likely to find it there. He flung open the top half of the door, and saw the horse lying so still. It proved beyond doubt that something was gravely wrong, but he could not understand what had happened to his father.

'Dad!' he shouted, and ran towards the alarm bell which was fastened outside the Night Shed. '*Dad!*' he bellowed again, and suddenly the door of Jenkins's flat opened and the head lad called:

'What's the matter, Syd?'

'Mr Jenkins, come down quick! Something's happened to Silver Monarch, and I can't find Dad.'

'Ring that bell!' ordered Jenkins, and swung away from the window.

*   *   *

'I don't think I'm really in the mood for three-handed whist,' said Kathleen Russell. 'Somehow it lacks the excitement of a foursome!' She made a face at her brother-in-law. 'I suppose I'll have to follow the barbarian country habits and go to bed. What time is it?'

'Half past ten,' answered Daphne, and stifled a yawn.

'I know, early to bed is catching,' said Kathleen. 'Even I

begin to get tired when the look in John's eyes says that it's bedtime.'

Gale was collecting the cards.

'I'll put a kettle on, and we'll all——' he began, and then heard the strident ringing of the general alarm bell from the stables. He stood absolutely still. Daphne put her hand to her mouth, stifling an exclamation.

'What is it?' asked Kathleen. 'What's the matter?'

'Stand by that telephone,' Gale said, and raced towards the door to the back of the house. His dark hair glinted under the light as he reached the door and pulled it open. His footsteps thudded, and the alarm still sounded, as if someone was determined to rouse everyone within earshot.

'What *is it*?' demanded Kathleen.

'It's Shoestring, I'll bet it is Shoestring,' Daphne exclaimed. 'I *hate* that horse!'

Gale was out of the house by then, and running along the path which led from the back garden of his house into the big stable yard. He heard voices and saw lights as he reached the side gate; it was locked. As he shouted, he heard the footsteps of a man approaching, and Jenkins called out:

'That you, Mr Gale?'

Who the hell did he think it was?

'Yes. What's wrong?'

Jenkins opened the gate. 'It couldn't be much more wrong, Mr Gale,' he said in a shocked voice. 'It's Silver Monarch, and he's dead. And if that isn't bad enough . . .'

Gale did not hear the rest, but went past the men towards the boxes. A dozen lads were in sight, and lights were going on all round the yard. Horses were moving about, one lad was quietening the big hunter, which was always troublesome when disturbed at night. Young Syd Cartwright was by the open door of Silver Monarch's box; he stared at Gale.

Gale said thinly: 'Where's your father?'

'I don't know, Mr Gale.'

'Go and find him.'

'Mr Gale, I—'

'*Go and find him!*' Gale shouted, glaring at the lad. Then he stepped into the box, although realizing that there was nothing he could do. Two other lads were already there. They had altered the position of the horse so that Gale could see, and what he saw seemed absolutely unbelievable. Silver Monarch had been shot in the side of the head; there was little sign of blood.

One of the lads said, in a husky voice: 'We can't find Ted Cartwright, Mr Gale.'

It was useless to say that Cartwright ought to be here; useless to rail at these lads, or at young Syd. Gale felt as if he had been stunned; that nothing worse could have happened. The horse with which he was to have made his name, the horse entrusted to him as a special favour by one of the leading owners, a horse worth a fortune, was lying there – a hulk of worthless flesh.

Gale knew that the two lads were watching him, saw the way the other lads watched, too. He stepped towards the door. Young Syd was standing there as if he hadn't moved; a frightened boy of sixteen. Gale made himself look at the lad more calmly.

'What happened, Syd?'

The boy tried to speak, but could not.

'Take your time,' Gale encouraged and looked around. 'Where's Mr Jenkins?'

'Gone to phone the police,' a lad answered.

Of course; it was a good thing someone kept his head.

'Well, Syd?'

'I don't know what happened, Mr Gale, I swear I don't. I was reading, and Dad was looking through the newspapers. He said it was a quarter past ten, time for the rounds. I was near an exciting part in the book, so I said I'd go later. Dad went out, and nothing happened for ten minutes, and he's usually back in five, so I went to see what was the matter.'

The boy was talking very jerkily, and his hands were unsteady; he kept putting them up in front of his mouth. 'I called out "Dad," I called out, and then I saw someone at the door, over there.' Syd pointed. 'And he went out and banged the door. I looked out, and there was a car moving off, I saw its rear light, that's all.'

'Did you see what make it was?'

'It was an old car, I think, the engine was knocking a lot,' Syd answered, 'but that's all I can tell you, Mr Gale. I ran straight across to see Silver Monarch. I thought if there was any trouble that's where it would be. As soon as I saw the horse lying down, I called for Mr Jenkins. He told me to raise the alarm, sir.'

Gale had studied the lad all the time, and new thoughts began to thrust aside something of the horror of what had happened. Old Cartwright was one of the most trustworthy men alive, and there was not the slightest chance that he would have betrayed his employer. He was the kind who would defend a horse with his life, too. It was an odd thought. Gale felt a constriction at his throat, although he knew that everyone was expecting him to speak. Then he saw Jenkins, and Daphne just behind him. That broke the spell, and he moved towards them.

'I talked to Inspector Hooper in person,' Jenkins said. 'He's on his way, Mr Gale.'

'Thanks.' Gale pressed a hand against his forehead. 'Has Jenkins told you, Daff?'

He could not understand the stony way in which she looked at him.

'Yes,' she said.

'It's unbelievable.'

'It isn't unbelievable at all,' Daphne said, in a hard bitter voice. 'It's exactly what you ought to have expected.'

'Daff, don't—'

'And don't tell me that you didn't jump to the truth as soon as I did,' Daphne said, in the same hard voice; she looked as if she hated everyone in sight. 'Silver Monarch was killed in mistake for that other horse. She said that she would kill it, and she meant exactly what she said.'

'My God!' breathed Gale.

'If I had that woman here,' Daphne went on, 'I think I would—'

'Daff, take it easy,' Gale protested urgently. 'We don't know anything for certain yet, this is only guesswork.'

'Take it easy!' his wife echoed, and suddenly stormed at him. '*Take it easy*, when everything you've worked for for fifteen years is in ruins at your feet! *Take it easy!* How you can stand there and say that I don't know. You can't realize what's *happened*. This will ruin you, don't you understand? No owner will ever trust you with a horse which is worth anything, you'll spend the rest of your life training old crocks, if you don't have to become a stable lad. When I think—'

Gale said: 'I know, Daff, it's bad,' and quite suddenly she was still and silent, huddled against him, while he was aware of the ring of eyes about them, of the open door which showed dead Silver Monarch and a lad still beside the horse. The night had lost all reality and all peacefulness. Daff was quivering against him, knowing that she had lost her head, hating herself for it, and with young Syd Cartwright so frightened, and his father missing.

Then one of the lads in Silver Monarch's box came running, and Gale could tell from the expression on his face that the worst was not over yet.

'What is it?' he demanded.

'I'm afraid we've found old Ted,' the lad said, and looked with great compassion on the dead man's son. 'Will you come over, sir, please?'

CHAPTER IV

SUPERINTENDENT WEST

FOR SUPERINTENDENT 'Handsome' West of the Yard, it was a gay morning despite the rain; a gay morning despite the wind; and a gay morning despite the fact that he knew his desk would be piled high, mostly with routine matters which might keep him locked to his desk most of the day. He had dreamed of being a superintendent of the Criminal Investigation Department for ten years and had been one for six months; and he was not yet used to the fact. It still thrilled him, and that despite the fact that he knew that to be 'thrilled' in such circumstances smacked of the boy rather than the man. He relished the 'good morning, Superintendent,' which came from right and left, first as he arrived and then as he went up the flight of stone steps, into the Yard building, and in the lift and along to his own office.

True, this was not exactly luxurious.

In fact it was little more than a box, with his desk squeezed into one corner, and an even smaller desk for a detective inspector or, occasionally, a sergeant whose job was to help with the chores. Yet it had a window on the VIP side of the Yard, and by craning his neck the new superintendent could just see the river and a section of Westminster Bridge. Also, it had a carpet, two filing cabinets, some reference books, a dictaphone, four telephones and a corner cupboard in which he kept personal possessions, such as the bottle of whisky for late-night sessions, a tin of biscuits for those times when he could not get out or even to the canteen to eat, spare cigarettes, and the oddments which might come in useful.

When he entered that morning, the office was empty, and there was a mass of unopened correspondence on his desk, as well as a sheaf of memoranda from other superintendents or from various departments. For the first time he looked a little rueful, but soon he grinned. He had a film star's good looks, hence his nickname, and the grey somehow failed to make any impression on his wiry, fair hair. He had a briskness of movement which might have been envied by a man of thirty, whereas he was now forty-one. When he took his heavy, belted raincoat off and hung it on a hook behind the door, then slapped his trilby on to the same peg, he proved to be tall and broad-shouldered, but tapering towards the waist, and surprisingly lean-hipped.

Before picking up the folded newspapers by the side of his chair, he glanced through the inter-office memos, made sure there was none from the Commander, CID or from the Assistant Commissioner, and began to go through the newspapers. He concentrated only on cases which affected the Yard, then skimmed the unofficial story of the nation's crime, which had no surprises although one item in the stop press of several newspapers had caught his eyes. It ran:

Famous Racehorse Killed. Silver Monarch, likely favourite for next year's Derby, found killed at Arncott Stables at Arncott, nr Reading, where John Gale trains.

'Killed,' mused Roger, and wondered if the word was intended to convey the slightly sinister ring that it undoubtedly had.

Then he began to open the mail.

There was very little of importance; most of the letters were notes from people he had questioned, or from County police forces offering or asking for information. The memoranda were much the same.

'Might be able to take an afternoon off,' he murmured to himself, and then grinned; a day off during the week hadn't been possible for six months; something always cropped up. The telephones were almost suspiciously quiet now, but he did not complain.

Then one rang.

'West speaking.'

'I'm sorry to worry you, Mr West, but Mrs Goff telephoned to say that Detective Sergeant Goff has a temperature, and she's had to send for the doctor.'

'Oh. Call her back, say I'm sorry, ask if there's anything they want.'

'Yes, sir.'

Goff was this week's duty-sergeant, but with the desk unlittered Roger could hardly call for a substitute. It meant that he ought to hang about the office most of the time. Pity. He picked up a packet of cigarettes, hesitated, and put it back into his pocket. He was smoking too much, and making a determined effort to cut down.

Another telephone bell rang.

He lifted the receiver. 'West.'

'Morning Handsome,' a man said. 'You awake?'

'Let's say I'm waking,' Roger answered, and was wary; for the speaker was Commander Hardy; Hardy was fond of his little joke, but often it had a hidden sting.

'How would you like to have a nice rest in the country?' he asked. 'You haven't done a job outside London since you had your own office, have you?'

'How nasty is this one?' asked Roger cautiously.

'Oh, not beyond your powers. It's a job in Berkshire, at Arncott.'

'Now, listen,' Roger protested, 'I'm no expert in racing matters. Why don't you send Uncle Percy? He can tell the front from the rear end of a horse, and knows all the jargon, too.'

'We've all got to learn,' said Hardy, and went on in a slightly marvelling voice: 'What makes you think it's anything to do with racing?'

'I read the stop press, about Silver Monarch's death.'

'That all?'

'Yes.'

'You didn't know that a stable lad was killed, at the same time?'

Roger said very slowly: 'No, I didn't. Silver Monarch's lad?'

'I'm not sure.'

'Has Berkshire called us in?'

'Yes,' replied Hardy. 'There's a rumour flying around near Arncott which they don't like. It concerns one of the county VIP's, and they think it might be wise to impress the local inhabitants with some Yard chaps. How about it? You haven't much on your plate at the moment, have you?'

'Just the chores. Goff's off ill, though.'

'I'll find somebody to take his place,' promised Hardy. 'And I imagine you would like to take Uncle Percy down with you.'

'Believe me I would – thanks!'

'I'll fix it,' promised Hardy. 'You tidy up everything you can, and come along and see me, will you?'

'In ten minutes,' promised Roger.

He rang off, picked up the papers which he had already singled out for attention, and began to make notes for whoever was going to take Goff's place. In each case Roger wanted some specific thing done, such as finding a witness, getting details of a man's past, checking with the provincial police. He was thinking that Hardy had been almost too affable; when Roger had been a Chief Inspector, he had had to mind his p's and q's with the Commander, which was hard to forget. Uncle Percy, or Detective Inspector Percy Snell, was exactly the right man for this job, of course. He had worked the tracks near London for twenty-five years, and knew nearly everything there was to know. He was a good sort to work with, too, a man who had no desire to get any higher; and he was good-humoured and thorough. If he had a fault it was that he relished his pint too much, but he had learned to discipline himself when on duty.

At ten o'clock exactly, Roger went into Hardy's office. At

twenty minutes past, he left it again, briefed as thoroughly as he could be, knowing much about the rumour already spreading that Silver Monarch had been killed in mistake for another, unknown horse, called Shoestring.

'Ever heard of this Shoestring?' inquired Roger of Percy Snell.

Snell was a man of forty-five who looked thirty-five, had a bright manner, was thin rather than spare, always dressed neatly but was a little too loud with his ties, socks and shirts. Now he wore a pale brown suit, well cut and admirably pressed, a red and blue striped shirt and a red-spotted tie, and socks of the same shade of red.

'Never heard of anything else,' he replied. 'I live on it.'

'We're being serious,' Roger said. He was in his office, checking over his case and making sure that he had everything he needed, from fingerprint powder to a magnifying glass, a steel tape and small plastic envelopes. The case, rather like an elaborate doctor's chest, contained all the tools and equipment he was likely to need on the spot at any investigation; it was standard at the Yard, plus a few oddments which he liked to take round with him.

'I gotta n'idea,' said Snell. 'Golden Shoes and Laces. Goes back a bit, but it could be – two of old Lord Foley's forlorn hopes. I'd say that this probably belongs to young Foley, at Foley Hall.'

'Right,' said Roger appreciatively. 'How far do you go back in the stud book?'

'Don't ask me,' said Snell. 'This the Arncott job?'

'Yes.'

'Damned shame about that Silver Monarch, bloody good piece of horse-flesh,' declared Snell. 'If it wasn't for the fact that the odds would have been so short that it wouldn't be worth putting half a crown on, I'd have backed it every time it went to the post. Bet this'll give John Gale hell.'

'The trainer?'

'Yes. Nice chap, but a bit too optimistic, if you know what

I mean,' said Snell. 'Used to train for the Duke of Midhampton, but had a bad run. Took over the old Arncott Stables, about three years ago that was, I suppose. Married Daphne Prentice.'

'The actress?'

'That's one word. She couldn't act pussy, but can she sing and roll her eyes! That's the girl. Lived happy ever after, they say.'

'Gale successful now?'

'Might be, one day.'

'Any advantage to him to have Silver Monarch dead?'

'Now listen, Handsome,' said Snell, forgetting that the 'Handsome' was usually reserved for times when Roger was out of earshot, 'it would be as much advantage to him as it would be an advantage to us if they stopped paying our wages. It's hell for John Gale – I can guarantee that in advance. Tell you what, I'll have a word with a pal of mine on the *Racecourse*, he'll know who's down at Arncott with Gale; amazing how much these tipsters get to know. How are we going? Train or—'

'I'll be downstairs in my car in twenty minutes.'

'Good-o,' said Snell. 'Just my luck to have a drive in the country on a day when you can hardly see your hand before your face. Anything special for me to do?'

'No.'

'Going to be a busman's holiday, this is,' said Snell. 'Or is it honeymoon?' He went to the door, hesitated, and then looked over his shoulder. 'Tell you one thing, Super.'

Roger smothered a grin.

'Yes?'

'If I'm right about Shoestring, he's owned by Lionel Foley, only son of the late Lord Foley and Lady F. who's very much alive. No need to go into the uneasy marital life of the old boy, but I can tell you this – Lady Foley always hated racehorses and everything to do with them, and if her only son decided to follow in Papa's footsteps she will kick up hell. I know her ladyship of old. Terror of the Turf they used to call her; once she actually chewed the noble lord up in front of the Royal Box. Perfectly normal woman in all other respects, but she couldn't take it when his nibs put everything but the ancestral home on a horse.'

'How serious is all this?' demanded Roger.

'Never more so. Anyone with a proper general knowledge including all matters relating to the Turf ought to know about it,' Snell asserted solemnly. 'I'll see what else I can pick up. Wouldn't care to give me an hour, would you?'

Roger said: 'Yes. Then ask someone to run you out to my place. I'll go and get a bag for the night. You'd better lay on a toothbrush and a pair of pyjamas, too.'

'How long for? A week or a month?'

'Guess,' said Roger.

A little before eleven o'clock, he drew up in front of his small detached house in Bell Street, Chelsea. This had been new when he had moved into it, and the street had been new, too; now it had a weathered look, the trees were old and spreading, the hedges between the dozens of small gardens were thick and excluding; but when Janet came to the door, after seeing him out of the window, the dustcap she had twisted round her head somehow took years away and she looked nearer twenty-five than forty. Roger stopped for a moment, to stare at her, as she said:

'Don't tell me how lovely I look. You've come to tell me you won't be home, or something like it.'

'Why don't you take over my job, you'd do it by intuition,' said Roger. 'I don't expect it will be more than a night or two, sweet, and it's only at Arncott, near Reading. I can get home at nights sometimes if it looks like being a long job. Come and help me pack a few things.'

'You go and put a kettle on, we might as well have a cup of tea,' said Janet resignedly. 'I don't know what the boys will say, they were counting on a night out with us.'

'They'll forgive me,' Roger assured her. 'Tell them it's a

case with a too-demanding mother, they'll know what a job I've got on, then.'

'What kind of case?' inquired Janet, and then her face paled, and she said tautly: 'Arncott, of course. It's that race-horse and stableman, or whatever they call them. It was on the eleven o'clock news headlines. Apparently he was very badly injured, darling. Don't—'

'Take risks, I know,' Roger said, almost flippantly.

He was taken aback at Janet's sharp reaction.

'Don't be so smug! Policemen have been killed before now, and you've been hurt often enough.'

'But my sweet, I'll be all right,' Roger assured her, and watched as she turned and hurried upstairs; he knew that there was a film of tears in her eyes, and it never failed to surprise him that she should live so constantly in this fear for him.

The need for such fear seldom occurred to him.

When she waved to him and Snell, from the front door, she was bright and cheerful enough and Snell probably hadn't the faintest idea that she had been so affected.

Snell was truly smug.

'I've really got something, my *Racecourse* pal hints at it in his 'Round the Stables' column this morning. There's no doubt that Lady F. actually threatened to kill Shoestring, and Shoe-string was in the next stall but one to Silver Monarch. The story came from Colonel Madden, Lady Foley's brother. He's an old soak who's lost every penny he ever had on horses and women, type who'll do anything for a fiver.'

'Did he hear the threat to Shoestring?'

'Yes. So did a dozen or so guests at a cocktail party. You won't be staying the night, Handsome – I bet we'll have it all sewn up by tea-time. It's one of those that come on a plate.'

'Like to bet on it?' asked Roger.

'What odds?'

'Evens.'

There was a pause. Then:

'Knowing how long you can take over questioning a single

witness, I'd want tens,' said Snell cautiously. 'I'd feel cheated, even then. That's what his deceased nibs was always telling Lady F. – she couldn't tell one horse from another. You can't want anything plainer than that, can you?'

'There's one small point you've overlooked, or else no one told you about it,' Roger said. 'The stable lad, Syd Cartwright, says he saw a *man* going out of the yard.'

'Come off it,' rejected Snell scornfully. 'It was a very poor light, the kid was on the other side of the yard, that would be seventy or eighty yards or so. I know that set-up, was out there ten years ago over a doping job. The kid was scared, and couldn't be absolutely sure whether it was a man or a woman, especially when so many women wear trousers these days. Any woman could dress up as a man and get away with it at that distance. Complicating things for the sake of it, that's what you're doing.'

'I'll tell you when I've seen that boy,' Roger said. 'He's obviously our main hope. There's no sign of the gun, but they've got the bullet out.' He stopped talking and concentrated on driving for the next ten minutes while Snell looked through his notes. They were at the end of the Great West Road, heading for Slough, when the radio crackled. Snell leaned forward, switched on, and said:

'Superintendent West's car.'

'Just had a message from Reading,' the Yard's information room reported dispassionately. 'The son of the murdered man Cartwright seems to be missing.'

There was a moment's silence; then Snell breathed:

'*Gawd.*'

CHAPTER V

MAIN WITNESS

SYD CARTWRIGHT woke that morning with a sense of dread which he did not at first understand. He was not in his own bed, one of a dozen in a large dormitory shed near the stables, but in a small room. The sun was shining across a corner of the window, and striking the wall just near his eyes; he did not realize that it was shining on his forehead. He heard none of the familiar sounds of the stable yard, and knew that he should have been awake hours ago, before full daylight. He pushed back the bedclothes, then fell heavily on the pillows.

It was as if he had been struck with a heavy weapon.

He *remembered*.

He had seen his father when they had cleared the straw away; seen his head, battered. None of the others near had realized that he was in the box.

He closed his eyes.

Hideous pictures came to mind, of his father and of the horse, which was also dead. Then he began to remember all that had happened, and the fact that he had let his father go out when he, Syd, should have gone; he had wanted to finish a chapter in a book.

He screwed up his eyes, but tears forced their way through. He fought to keep back the sound of crying, but could not. He was not yet seventeen. He could not remember his mother, who had died before he could walk. He could remember only his father and horses; here at Arncott, at Newmarket, at Lambourne – five or six different stables, but always his father and horses – the only living creatures which really mattered to him. He had the inborn sense of love for the sleek beauty of coat and muscle, for the exultant feeling of a horse between his legs, the unbelievable rhythm of the horse's movement as it galloped, the sense of oneness and an exhilaration which had amounted almost to exaltation.

None of these things had been learnt; they had grown into part of him.

And of all the horses he had ever helped to do and longed to ride, Silver Monarch was the greatest.

He began to cry through his clenched teeth, fighting away the picture, hating himself for what seemed to be weakness, and lying on his back with the brightness all about him.

He heard a sound of footsteps, near the door.

He flung himself round and buried his face in the pillow, biting into the linen and the feathers to choke the crying. He still heard the footsteps, of a woman. He realized, without consciously thinking of it, that he was in Mr Gale's house. The footsteps stopped at the door. He hoped no one would come in, he hoped to God no one would come; he didn't want to be seen like this, he couldn't stand it.

The footsteps passed.

The interruption had helped him, and his body relaxed a little. He eased his head, so that he could breathe more freely, then turned over on his side, sniffling, and looking at the door. The woman passed again, and went into another room. He sat up. Over in a corner was a wash-hand basin, and he was anxious to wash away the stains of tears. He got up, staggering a little as he went towards the basin, but quickly he ran the cold tap, and doused his head and face. His hair was cut very short, and would take little time to dry. He went away from the basin towards the window, and could see over the roofs of the actual stables. From here he overlooked the path leading from the garden of Mr Gale's house to the stable yard; he could also see the clock, and could even glimpse the main road and the top of the gate where he had seen the man last night.

If only he had been closer. If only he had got a good look at the car. He recalled that throbbing note, and the knocking, an engine he felt sure he would recognize and which he had heard before. If only he could remember where.

Then he realized that he felt hungry.

He had no watch, and there was no clock in the room, the tower clock was just out of sight; but it struck, and he waited and counted ... 'nine, ten.' Ten o'clock, and he ought to have been up at half past six, starting to muck-out! He felt a moment of panic which faded when he remembered where he was and what had happened; he could just recall Mrs Gale saying to a police sergeant that 'the boy must go to bed, it was after three o'clock', and she had brought him up here herself.

There had been another woman with them; her sister.

Syd was wearing pyjamas which were too big for him. His own clothes, pants, singlet, grey flannels and a grey knitted sweater were on a chair, with his shoes beside them; it had been a kind of edict of his father's that he should change out of breeches, boots and leggings after tea each day.

He dressed quickly, opened the door very slowly and cautiously, and found himself on a large landing, where there were several other doors, and from which a passage led to another flight of stairs. Once or twice he had been downstairs in this house, but he had never been up here before. He crept out. The woman was silent, and he wondered if she had gone downstairs, and whether it had been Mrs Gale, her sister, or one of the maids. He reached the half-landing, where there was a wide window overlooking the heath. Suddenly he caught his breath, for a mile away he saw a string of horses walking, each with a boy up. It was late, but this was the usual morning's exercise on the heath – one of the highlights of the day. Twice he had led Silver Monarch.

Tears threatened again.

He fought them back, and turned towards the second section of the stairs, then stopped abruptly. Mrs Gale's sister, he could never remember her name, was at the foot of the stairs, smiling up. She looked very pretty. She had brown hair, brushed down to her shoulders, and blue eyes.

'Good morning, Syd.'

'Good morning, Miss.'

'Did you sleep well?'

'Yes, thank you.'

'I expect you're feeling hungry.'

'I suppose I am.'

'Cook's going to get your breakfast as soon as you go to the kitchen.'

'Thank you,' Syd said.

He knew that he sounded stiff and awkward, and felt embarrassed and almost childish, but there was nothing he could do about that. He started down the stairs. He wished Mrs Gale's sister would go, would stop looking at him; and she turned away, as if she sensed what was in his mind.

'You know where the kitchen is, don't you?'

'Yes, thank you.'

'I'll tell Mr Gale you're up,' she promised, and looked at him again. 'Syd, I just want to tell you this; you're among friends. We know we can't do much to help, but we all want to do everything we can. You'll remember that, won't you?'

'Yes, Miss, thank you,' he said huskily.

He did not think much about that as he went into the kitchen, the most familiar of all the rooms in this house. Until two months ago there had been a fifteen-year-old maid whom he'd rather liked, but she had got a factory job at Reading. He knew the cook, and her sharp tongue and her competence. He seemed to shrink a little, because he expected pity from her, and already knew that he did not want pity. But she looked across and said brusquely:

'It's about time, ten more minutes and you wouldn't have had more than a piece of toast.'

'Sorry I'm late,' he said.

'I'll let you off this time. You know where to find the knives and forks. Set yourself a place at the corner of the table.'

'Ta,' Syd said, and obeyed as she cracked eggs into a frying pan. Soon bacon was sizzling, and Syd felt more hungry than ever; in a queer way, that seemed to be wrong. By the time the two eggs, bacon and a sausage were in front of him, he was ravenous, right or wrong. There were hunks of new white bread and some yellow, salted, farmhouse butter. He ate rapidly, trying to remember that he wasn't in the big communal dining-room, where the stable lads paid very little attention to table manners; here he ought to be on his best behaviour.

He had just finished when Mrs Gale's sister came in.

'Well, his appetite's all right, anyhow,' Cook said.

Syd jumped up.

'Mr Gale's in the yard,' Kathleen told him. 'He'd like you to go and see him there.'

'Yes, Miss, thank you ever so,' Syd gabbled.

He was glad to be out of the kitchen, although he knew that both women were looking at him through the kitchen window. He did not glance round. The walk from here to the stable yard, where the small gate leading from this garden was open, seemed a long one. He did not know exactly what was in his mind. There was a kind of ache in him, because he remembered what he had lost, but the vividness of the hideous picture had faded. It was more a sense that he would never find things the same which harassed him.

Four men, all big and therefore unfamiliar, were in the yard; big men were seldom there, except when owners and visitors arrived. Syd recognized one of the policemen whom he had seen last night, the man who had questioned him. He was talking to Mr Gale. Gale stood square and solid with his back to the box where the horse and Syd's father had been found dead. It was obvious that men were working inside. Straw had been put outside, and everything from the stable had been spread on the brickwork, which had been cornered off so that no one could step over it. The dozens of small things kept in a stable, but which one forgot, were there: pitch-fork, knife, spare reins, spare parts of saddles, an old saddle, two rows of medallions and cups, a pair of old thigh boots . . .

Those were his father's.

Tears stung his eyes.

Mr Gale looked across at him, and the big detective stopped talking. It was as if everyone was staring at Syd. None of the horses was in, and he was seldom here when the horses and the lads were out; that added to the oddness of the situation.

'Good morning, sir,' he made himself say.

''Morning, Syd,' greeted Mr Gale, quite briskly. 'You remember Chief Inspector Hooper, don't you?'

'Yes, sir. Good morning, sir.'

' 'Morning Cartwright,' the detective said. He had a large nose, and looked as if he drank a lot; his eyes were dark blue and rather beady, and there were many small red veins in them. 'Sleep well?'

'Yes, thanks.'

'Good. Remember what I asked you last night?'

'Yes.'

'I know you want to help us catch these devils as soon as we can,' Chief Inspector Hooper said. 'Have you remembered anything else?'

'No,' Syd answered, very clearly. 'I've been trying to think, all the way from Mr Gale's house. I'm sure I told you everything.'

'You didn't recognize the man?'

'No.'

'Sure it was a man?'

'I saw someone who wore a mackintosh, a cap and trousers,' Syd said, very carefully, 'and I saw a red light at the back of a big old car.'

'Sure it was big and old?'

'Well, it sounded like it,' Syd insisted. 'That's all I can tell you. It's no use me making anything up, is it?'

'Last thing you want to do,' put in Mr Gale. 'All right, Syd. Is there anything you want to do for the next hour or so? We want you to be handy, some detectives are coming out from Scotland Yard a bit later, and they'll want to see you. How about getting stuck into those cups? They've been waiting a fortnight.'

'Yes, sir.' Syd hesitated, and then made himself ask: 'Can I go into the Night Shed, sir?'

'Not yet. The Yard people want to have a look round first,' Mr Gale answered. 'There are a lot of formalities to attend to, but we'll lend you a hand with them, you needn't worry. We know what a bad packet you've had, Syd – we'll see you through.'

'Thank you very much,' Syd said.

The stilted words did nothing to ease his feelings. He crossed towards the tack room, where for weeks the cups had been in line for cleaning; a job which the younger lads always did. Tight-lipped, he glanced at the closed door of the Night Shed. The Arncott detective and Mr Gale were watching him, but he didn't look round; their sympathy was almost too apparent, and it hurt. He wanted to be somewhere by himself, where he could give vent to his feelings; and he wanted to strike out and to *hurt* ...

Something.

The other lads and the horses would be back by half past eleven, so he would not have long on his own. It was unusual for everyone to be out, and he had an idea that this had been arranged by the police. Not that it mattered. He went to his cubicle in the main dormitory for the younger lads, and changed into jacket, shirt and riding breeches, knotted his scarf with great precision, and put on his cloth cap; both were of black and white check.

Now he was dressed for the day's work.

He went into the big livery room, which was rather like a bare, unfurnished church, with hooks on the walls from which saddles of famous horses hung; and here were the trophies and accoutrements of horses which had been trained here over a period of a hundred years and more. In the early days he had felt a sense of awe, and that still lingered. There was nothing here belonging to Silver Monarch, except a noseband which had been damaged and which he had brought in himself. When he saw these, tears stung his eyes again. He stared fixedly at them, clenching his fists, hating the man who had killed that horse, *hating* him, realizing how terribly he missed the horse. He could 'see' it walking, imagine the feel of its smooth nose, seeing its teeth as it nibbled his palm for sugar, feeling it swell beneath him as he had ridden round the yard on it, watching it gallop over the heath, so sure – as the whole stable had been sure – that it was a wonder horse.

He turned away, and began to clean the irons, but it was too dull a job, he had too much time to think. He had to move about, walk, run, ride; that was the thing he wanted most, to fling his legs astride a horse, and gallop. If only he could! He dropped the rags and the polish, and went out again. The big detectives were all out of sight, but Mr Gale was talking to a tall, elderly woman, Lady Bartlett, who had three horses here. She turned and looked at Syd, and he could see the compassion in her eyes.

'Want anything, Syd?' Gale called.

'Is Marble in the paddock, sir?'

'Yes. Want to ride him?'

'It's time he had more exercise, sir.'

'All right, but don't let him jump.'

'I won't take any chances with him, sir,' Syd promised.

Marble was a small plater, a friendly, over-eager horse with the inclination to jump at the slightest opportunity. One of the younger boys had taken it out a few months ago, tried a fence, and pulled a tendon; but the leg was as sound as ever again, although it would be two or three weeks before Marble was taken out with the other horses. Syd went through the yard and along a passage on the other side of the yard from Mr Gale's house. He stepped through a small gate towards the smaller of the paddocks, which was fenced with chestnut paling. A dozen horses, mostly old and retired, were out here. Marble came up at once, a small grey with lines not unlike Silver Monarch; Syd had always liked a grey.

The big, rangy grey, Shoestring, was also in the paddock. Syd stared at it, a hand on the smaller horse's neck. He had heard something of what had been said the previous night, and knew that half of the lads were sure that Silver Monarch had been killed in mistake for Shoestring. He felt that he hated the horse; hated to see it standing there, head up, looking towards him with a kind of eagerness, as if it were boasting: 'Try me, I'm as good as the Monarch.'

Syd swung round, led Marble back to the yard, saddled him, tightened the girths, and got into the saddle. With a horse beneath him, he felt complete. He went back through the paddock. No one else was in sight, and the only sound he heard except the clip-clop of the horse beneath him was the stable clock, chiming eleven. He knew that he must not go far. All he wanted was a canter.

All he wanted was a *gallop*.

He gave the horse its head, and Marble seemed equally anxious to move fast; from trot to canter, then into a smooth gallop, not exerting himself but trying out that leg as if he was as anxious as Syd to make sure that he did not put too great a strain on it. He was going well; Marble always would. But he lacked the stamina of the outstanding horses, he was only a kind of image of Silver Monarch.

Syd reined him in.

Now he was a mile or so away from the paddock, on the open heath. A mile or more to the right he could see the main string of horses, on the other side of the road which led from Arncott to Foley Village. The stables were half way between these places, each of which was two or three miles away. Between here and Foley Village was the gate to Foley Hall, and close by it was Foley's Folly, the huge brick watch tower, built by the last earl in order to watch the horses exercising and galloping on the heath.

The main string of horses passed behind a copse of beeches. On this side of the road, near Syd, there were many more trees, sometimes thick copses; that was why the serious training was done on the other side of the road.

Syd satisfied himself that Marble was not blown, and then

set him to another gallop. There was a half-mile stretch between copses which would not be too much of a test for any horse. In a strange way, Syd seemed to have forgotten much of what had happened; he was almost happy, and could confine his thoughts to the horse, to the task of riding, to using his judgement of condition. He was applying some of the lessons which his father had taught him, but was not thinking of his father.

He slowed down as he passed the half-mile post, from where he could see the tower, with the sun reflecting from the windows and the observation platform, and began to turn. Then he saw a car, with two men standing beside it, inside a clearing in a patch of wooded land near him. It did not surprise him. Men often hid here, keeping their car out of sight, while watching the horses on the other side of the main road; here were the tipsters, the journalists, the touts, who wanted to make quite sure of the form of every horse entered for any race. There was no way of stopping it, and Mr Gale took little notice.

One of these men was very tall and thin.

'Come here a minute,' he called.

There was no reason at all why Syd should not; there would probably be a proffered half-crown and a request for information; it was all part of the day's work. He did not give that a second thought as he turned the horse towards the two men.

'What are you after?' he demanded, and he had not spoken so normally all the morning.

The thin man said: 'Are you Syd Cartwright?'

'Supposing I am?'

'No lip,' the man said. 'You are, aren't you?' He paused, and Syd saw the other man, a shorter, heavier man, moving towards the other side of the car; and incidentally, moving to a position which was behind him and Marble. On another morning, he would probably have told them where to get off, turned Marble, and galloped away. Instead, he said stiffly:

'Yes, I'm Syd Cartwright.'

D.R.—3

'Too bad about your Pa, Kid,' the thin man said, and the other man was now within three yards of Syd and the horse. 'That right you saw the man who did it?'

'Supposing——' Syd began.

'Listen, I'm from the *Globe*. A story will be worth a pony to you,' the thin man said. 'You'll need plenty of money now you're on your own. It's not as if I'm asking for information about the stable, I'm not interested in form, the sporting-page boys can have that. I'm a crime reporter, Syd, and I'm on serious business. Did you see the man who killed your father and that horse?'

Syd said: 'Yes, I did.' He felt a kind of anger, because the man had tried to reduce his loss to pounds, shillings and pence, but that emotion did not strike very deeply. He turned the horse – and found the thickset man holding the reins and staring up at him intently.

'I'm not going to talk about it,' he went on.

'Police told you not to?'

'Perhaps they did, perhaps they didn't,' Syd said.

There was a moment's silence, broken by the sound of a car engine starting up. On that instance, Syd recognized the knocking noise, and he was quite sure that it was the murderer's car. His eyes burned and he cried:

'Stop that car! We've got to stop that car!' He snatched at the reins, but before he could urge the horse on, the thin man grabbed his arm, and held the reins.

The car moved off, still hidden by the trees.

'Let me go!' cried Syd. 'That's the car the murderers got away in!'

The other did not let him go; and that was the first moment of alarm.

Syd tugged. 'Don't you understand? That's the car I heard last night!'

Instead of answering, the thin-faced man moved forward swiftly, while the other dropped the reins and snatched at

Syd's wrist. Syd tried to free himself, but the man's grip was too powerful.

He was being pulled down, and suddenly realized that there was acute danger. He did not so much understand as sense it.

He no longer heard the car, and could think only of this sudden cause of fear. Without conscious thought, he remembered a lesson his father had taught him to meet an emergency if he were thrown. He let himself go, tucked his head down, and turned his right shoulder towards the ground, right arm hugged almost into his chest. The other man was so surprised that he released his hold. Syd hit the ground and rolled over and over, protecting himself as if other horses might be racing up to trample him. Then he bounded to his feet, ten yards away from where he had fallen. The thin man was still staggering away, obviously Marble had pushed against him; Marble was between the stocky man and Syd.

'Marble! Come on!' Syd called, and whistled desperately. 'Marble!' He backed away as the thin man grabbed at the reins; but the man was too late, and Marble came trotting.

Then the man made another futile grab.

'Come on,' Syd almost screamed, and the horse drew near enough to be mounted. Syd leapt up. The thin man came lurching forward, but missed by a foot. Syd swung the horse round on its haunches, and gave it its head; it raced forward, and the wind stung Syd's eyes and ears and felt sharp and cold against his face. Then he saw the branch of a tree loom up, just in front of him. Fear surged up again. He flung up his arms to protect his face, then crashed into the branch, and was sent flying from the saddle.

Then he heard the men running towards him.

CHAPTER VI

SEARCH

ROGER WEST saw the uniformed policeman standing near the open gate beneath the clock tower of the Arncott Stables, and slowed down. Snell said: 'Here we are,' purposelessly, and settled back in his seat as if this were what he had been looking forward to. Roger slowed down, and held out his card to the police constable, who said:

'Mr Hooper's on the scene of the crime now, sir.'

Roger kept a straight face.

'Thanks. That stable lad turned up?'

'Afraid not, sir.'

Roger said: 'Pity,' and drove into the yard. There were a dozen diminutive men or youths in sight, all of them grooming horses, half in and half out of the boxes. It was a long time since Roger had seen so many horses together. His first impression was of cleanliness and tidiness; some beds of wallflowers were in the middle of the yard, surrounded by crescents of short, close-cut grass. But there was the inescapable horsey smell which seemed to push the sharp freshness of the air aside. Snell sniffed.

'Now that's what I call perfume,' he observed. 'That's the real stuff, Super.'

'You ought to bottle some.' Roger saw the group of men round a stable at the far end, and drove slowly towards them. There were about thirty boxes, shaped in a wide circle with the dirt road between them and the grass and flowers. At the far end two roads led off on either side of a large wooden building, and other brick and wooden buildings were on the right and left.

'That's the Night Shed,' Snell explained. 'Place where they sit up all night if there's any trouble, or if there's a foal on the way. Where they guard from, too. That building on the right is the tack room. The one on the left is the sleeping quarters for the lads. This outfit's a hundred years old but you couldn't have it planned much better, could you?'

'No. Find out if there's a plan of it available. If not, do me a good sketch plan, showing all the ways in and out, give me the sizes, everything.'

'Right.'

Roger pulled up near the group of larger men, and by a stable where the brickwork immediately outside it had been cordoned off. He saw Hooper, whom he knew by reputation as shrewd and very capable, if uncouth; Hooper certainly looked uncouth, with his little eyes, rather loose mouth, and heavy barrel-like body.

'Superintendent West?'

'Chief Inspector Hooper?'

Roger got out, and they shook hands. Roger tried to size the man up, and came quickly to the conclusion that Hooper would like to be regarded as the fountain-head, so he asked:

'Any news of Syd Cartwright?'

'Not a trace,' Hooper answered. Obviously he was appraising Roger with the same kind of detachment; he had probably decided that the newcomer did not appear to match his reputation as the youngest superintendent at Scotland Yard. Then Hooper surprised Roger. 'My own fault, too. I ought to have kept a watch on the kid. Funny thing how you can be caught napping when you've been in the job forty years. If you're going to tear a strip off me, start now, while I know I deserve it.'

That was fine!

Roger grinned: 'Consider it done. No trace of him at all, you say?'

'Last we've heard of him he was seen galloping across the heath,' Hooper said. 'I've got a sketch plan of the neighbourhood drawn up; thought you'd need that.' Efficient was the word. 'It's over at the Night Shed. If it's all right with you we'll use that as the office while you're here. Better than being in the house, although Gale's offered us a room.'

'The shed sounds better.'

'Thing is, young Cartwright was eating his heart out,' Hooper went on. 'I can quite understand him wanting a gallop. He asked Gale, when I was present. Gale said okay, and told me that the boy was as safe on a horse as if he'd been born on one. He went out on one side of the heath, and the last time he was seen he was galloping hell for leather – much faster than Gale had expected him to go. Don't ask me why, but he might have been trying to ride the shock out. Disappeared behind some trees, and an hour afterwards his horse turned up by itself.'

'Injured?'

'Nope. Can't say we've done much else, either. There was a car about at the time, one or two of the lads exercising the horses saw it, but can't get a description. Witnesses were too far away. I—'

Roger saw Hooper's expression change suddenly, and become one almost of consternation. Snell had got out of the car on the other side, and had rounded it, and Hooper saw him for the first time.

'Strewth, did you have to bring *him*?' he demanded, in tones of deep disgust. 'I thought I'd seen the last of him on that doping job.'

'No one had to bring me,' Snell said airily, 'I was the person of their choice. How're you, me old cock?'

'Worried sick about this ruddy job,' Hooper answered. 'Ever since that kid disappeared I've been kicking myself, or did I say that before? I've had the whole of the district covered. Half of Gale's lads are out, searching in case the kid was thrown, and I've got a lot of the farmers around here on the look-out, too. If we don't find him by early afternoon I'm going to ask you to organize a proper hunt. We'll make everyone down tools and really get on with it.'

'So you think the murderer believes Syd Cartwright could identify him,' Roger hazarded.

'That's a possibility,' Hooper said, 'and I'm prepared to believe a man capable of any job if he can knock a man about like he did Ted Cartwright. One of the best, old Ted; many's the tip I've picked up from him. What do you want to do first, Mr West?'

'Have a quick look round, and meet John Gale and the other people here,' Roger answered.

It would do no good to join in the search for the missing lad; the quicker he met the people involved and could size the situation up for himself the better it would be. He let Hooper show him into the stable, saw how it had been cleaned up in the search for clues, and then went with Hooper towards the Night Shed. Hooper told him, gloomily, that there was still no trace of the gun, and the bullet taken from the dead horse's head was a ·32 which could have been fired from many different makes of gun. There had been comparatively little bleeding from old Cartwright's head wounds. No fingerprints or clues of any kind had been found.

'Except that noisy car Syd Cartwright heard last night,' Roger mused. 'You put that in the report to the Yard. And a car was seen just before he disappeared, too.'

'Cars do appear on roads,' Hooper said dryly. 'I've had a man going round to the garages, and about thirty old cars make the kind of noise Syd described. More big old cars than new little 'uns near here.'

Roger said: 'Pity.'

A constable was on duty outside the Night Shed, and stood aside for Hooper to unlock the door. Inside it was spotlessly clean. There were two camp-beds, one in each corner, a table, a small refrigerator, some books and magazines; Gale obviously believed in making sure that anyone on night duty was well looked after.

Pinned on a plain wooden wall was a large sketch map of the district. Another map on a larger scale included Arncott –

a town of five thousand people – Foley Village and the Arncott
Stables, halfway between. Marked on both was Foley Hall,
and a red dot was marked: *Foley's Folly – Watch-Tower*. A
five minutes' study of all this gave Roger a clear picture, while
Hooper and Snell studied him as much as they did the map.

Roger turned away.

'That's worth a day at least, thanks. How far has this
rumour about Lady Foley spread?'

'Land's End to John o' Groats,' Hooper answered.

'I mean locally.'

'It's common gossip. Gale heard her make the threat to
Shoestring, so did a dozen others. The threat was going the
rounds by yesterday morning, and when this news broke –
well, we're not so dumb, we country bumpkins, we put two and
two together.'

Roger said: 'What's your opinion?'

'Haven't got one, yet,' answered Hooper. 'I've known Lady
Foley on and off for fifteen years, and when she wants to do a
thing, she goes ahead and does it. She'd have killed Shoestring
if he'd stayed at the Hall, but here—' He shrugged. 'I don't
know. Depends how much she feared that her Lionel was going
the way of his poor lamented Dad. I can imagine she would
sneak down here, and I can imagine she would use a gun, but I
can't imagine her knocking Ted Cartwright about.'

'Does she own a gun?'

'Yes. Got a licence too. I can think of twenty people with
licences.' Hooper was almost too gloomy, as if he revelled in
negative news.

'Would she be strong enough to inflict the head injuries?'
Roger asked.

'Yes. But—'

'If she'd been caught in the act of killing the horse, she
might have been frightened into doing a lot of things you
wouldn't expect,' remarked Roger, deliberately saying the obvious.

'I daresay.'

'But you don't think she killed Cartwright?'

'I think you'll be wasting your time if you assume she did it in person,' answered Hooper, 'but I wouldn't put it past her to have paid someone else to kill the horse. If the someone was caught red-handed and recognized, then you've got a motive.'

'As soon as I've met the Gales and Jenkins, the head lad, I'll go and see Lady Foley,' Roger decided. 'I take it that the best way will be to come straight out with it.'

'The only way – no use beating about the bush with her ladyship.'

'Thanks,' said Roger. 'Searched the Hall and grounds for the stable lad?'

'No reason to, yet,' Hooper said. 'Give me an excuse, and I will. Now about the *dramatis personae*, as they say ...'

Roger listened closely while Hooper drew a brief word-picture of the others involved, then went to the trainer's house. John Gale had been asked to wait and see him. Gale's wife and sister-in-law were out on the heath searching for the missing boy.

Gale had little to say. He was a well-knit, biggish, capable-looking man, who gave the impression that he had taken a hard knock; there was that defensive look in his eyes which seemed to suggest it, and also wariness; factors which might be accounted for if he had any sense of guilt. Roger left him at the house, after five minutes. It was nearly two o'clock, and Snell said:

'Don't you ever get hungry?'

'You hungry already?' Roger glanced at his watch. 'Good Lord! All right, we'll have a snack, and then get to Foley Hall.' He was glad of a respite, for it enabled him to put everything he had seen and everyone he had met into focus. The fact that there was still no news of the boy Cartwright was the most worrying factor; the fear that he had been kidnapped and perhaps killed to silence him as a witness gave the case an uglier touch of the sinister.

One thing was clearly evident; the tension and the atmosphere at the stables.

'You go down to Foley Village after we've finished,' Roger said, 'and find out if there's anything worth picking up there. Find out if they feel the same as the training outfit does.'

'Take it from me they will,' Snell assured him. 'They live on racing. The whole village would be getting all its shirts ready for Silver Monarch. It'll be like a morgue down there.'

'Keep your ear to the ground,' Roger warned.

'Okay. What do you make of my old pal Hooper?'

'Follow his example and you'll be a detective one day.'

After a snack meal had been provided by two stable lads, Roger left the Night Shed, and walked round the yard to his car, now parked near the main gates. He had looked at these already, and seen the chalk marks made by the local police; photographs of everything found on there would be available later in the afternoon. He had the feeling of satisfaction which always came with the realization that the local police were fully efficient and co-operative.

Roger drove towards the heath where the missing boy had last been seen. It looked bright and attractive in the afternoon sun. In the distance he could see small groups of men walking, and nearer at hand a line of men and women were beating a copse, as if after birds. Dotted about the heath were individuals, obviously searching. He had the uneasy feeling, almost one of guilt, which always came whenever he knew that a search was on for a human being who might have been killed. That bare countryside seemed so vast, and threatened to hold too many secrets.

He saw the red brick of a tower, obviously Foley's Folly, long before reaching a narrow, paved road and a fingerpost which read: Foley Hall. He turned into this road and pulled in as near the tower as he could get. It was over a hundred feet high, massive and ugly, with small windows and, near the top, a kind of observation platform.

Had the police searched here?

Roger went to a narrow door, which was ajar, and stepped inside. In spite of the sun's brightness, it was gloomy in here. He went up a narrow spiral staircase, and it seemed to go on for ever, but at last, breathless, he reached the top. The view was magnificent. He could see the downs, Foley Village and, beyond Gale's stables the red roof, of Arncott, spreading deep into the countryside.

But there was no body, and no suggestion that the Folly had been used for crime.

The road was little more than a lane, with thick hedges on either side, and it ran upwards, twisting and turning. He drove cautiously, especially after he caught a glimpse of something moving, without being sure what it was. Then he reached a corner and saw two women, each astride a horse. From Hooper's description, he knew that these were Gale's wife and her sister. The smaller woman, the wife, had an almost china-like beauty which wasn't quite real. The other was bigger, younger, very fresh and attractive, but without such near-perfection. Roger waited for them to pass. Both smiled and said: 'Thank you,' but the smile was on the surface; he could see the gravity in their eyes.

They cantered on, once they were past him.

He soon came to the parkland, and slowed down when he saw the house. There were many like it in this part of England, and he knew a little of its history. It was mostly late eighteenth-century, built on the ruins of a Tudor palace. The Foleys had been granted the land by Henry VIII and the family had prospered in every way until the first world war.

At one time their racing colours, pale blue, claret and gold, had been among the most famous in the country; only between the wars had their fortunes begun to drop, had Foley thrown away his heritage on desperate gambles; but gambling and a love of horses had been part of the heritage. Roger now knew – thanks to Hooper – that only a small part of the house, the central rooms, was occupied; north-east and west wings were closed, and most of the rooms were empty.

The sun was shining on well-trimmed grass and spring flowers, all tended with a thoroughness which told of a gardener's pride. It might still have been the home of a wealthy family; but the herd of Herefords and another of Guernseys, in nearby fields, told how close to the house the farmland had encroached. The grey walls looked forbidding, and the tall windows dark as Roger drove up. He did not go to the front of the house, with its great porch and massive steps, but towards the side, which he had been told was the main entrance nowadays. He caught a glimpse of an old man in a vegetable garden some distance away, and as he drew up, a green-painted side door opened, and a tall, youthful-looking man came striding out.

He pulled up short.

Roger opened the car door.

'Good afternoon. Do you know if—'

The young man was not only tall but handsome in a rather effeminate way. His cheeks were flushed and his eyes looked too bright, as if he were in a wild temper. There was a curious gracefulness in his manner when he stopped.

'. . . Lady Foley is in?' Roger finished.

'She is unable to see anyone,' the young man announced abruptly.

This was undoubtedly Lionel, the son.

'I hope she'll see me,' Roger said, and showed his card.

Lionel looked down at it, then stepped back a pace; the anger seemed to freshen in his eyes.

'She won't see you or any policeman. She's sick to death of being pestered. If you know what's good for you, you'll go away and forget her.'

Roger said mildly: 'I don't think that would be very wise.'

'What do you mean?'

'It's never a good thing to have to ask anyone to come to us,' Roger explained pleasantly. 'It's much better for us to come to them in the first place. Ask Lady Foley to see me at once, please.' Authority became crisp in his voice.

Lionel hesitated; it seemed to Roger that he was the kind

likely to hesitate a great deal, often over matters which should be easy to decide. He would probably have much difficulty in making up his mind. Now he looked stubborn, and his curved lips were set.

'Do you have to pester her?'

'Yes.'

'If you believe that canard about her killing Silver Monarch in mistake for my horse, you're as crazy as the rest of the fools around here.'

'I don't believe anything until I've proof,' said Roger. 'What makes you so sure that the rumour is wrong, though? Didn't your mother threaten to kill your horse?'

Lionel said sharply: 'Supposing she did.'

'Isn't Silver Monarch much the same colour and size as Shoestring?'

'A blind man could tell the difference!'

'Could your mother tell them apart?'

'You come here pretending that you just want information, but you're as prejudiced as the rest,' Lionel said bitterly. 'You're simply wasting your time.'

'Then what do you think happened at Foley Stables last night, Mr Foley?'

'It's not my business to guess, it's yours to find out. You won't find the answer here, of that I'm—'

Foley broke off, seeing something which Roger hadn't noticed. Roger turned round, and saw two horsewomen approaching across the parkland, riding quite fast, and with a hint of urgency which seemed to reflect itself on Lionel Foley's face too. The two men waited, close to the steps. Roger recognized the china doll and her sister. It was remarkable how well the smaller woman rode; as if she and her horse were moulded together. She was carrying something which it was impossible to identify.

'What have they found?' Lionel asked, and he could not stop himself from striding forward.

Roger saw that it was an ordinary-looking cloth cap, of black and white check. It looked new.

Behind the wife of the trainer, the sister came more slowly. She was nothing like so sure a rider but looked lovely in the saddle, with the wind of her movement carrying her hair back from her shoulders and from her forehead.

'What is it, Mrs Gale?' Lionel called out, as soon as they were within earshot.

Roger seemed to hear the answer before it was spoken:

'It's Syd Cartwright's cap,' Daphne Gale called. 'We found it near a bush on one side of the drive.'

She didn't ask questions, except with her eyes. Roger realized what was in her mind, saw something like horror come into the eyes of Lady Foley's son. Lionel held up his hand for the cap, but Roger moved, and took it.

'May I?' He handled the cap gingerly. There were a few bramble thorns in it, and some strands of the material were pulled, but there was no sign of blood, nothing to suggest that its wearer had been injured when he had lost it.

Lionel was staring at it, still touched with that horror. He seemed to speak to himself as he asked:

'What was it doing here?'

'That's what we have to find out,' Daphne said, in a voice which told Roger that there was no love lost between them. She looked at Roger. 'You are the man from Scotland Yard, aren't you?'

'Yes.'

'I thought I recognized you from a photograph,' Daphne said. 'I'm Mrs Gale, and this is my sister, Miss Russell. Presumably you're the one man who can do something about this. I think it's time that the Hall and the grounds of the house were searched.'

Behind her, Kathleen said: 'Daff,' and let her voice trail off. In front of her, Lionel Foley looked as if he could snatch the cap from Roger's hand, and smother Daphne Gale with it.

Then the front door opened, and Lady Foley appeared.

CHAPTER VII

DISCOVERY

ROGER, SEEING Lady Foley for the first time, could imagine that everything he had been told about her was true. She was small; for a woman of nearly sixty she had a remarkably trim figure and a very small waist; many a girl of eighteen would have envied her bosom and the curves of her hips. She wore a plain navy-blue dress, simple but well cut, was well made-up and well groomed. She was still handsome Roger thought, and had the odd feeling that she was more manly than her willowy son.

Roger did not move, but let her son and the two women handle the situation.

'Lionel——' Lady Foley began, and then seemed to see Mrs Gale and Kathleen Russell for the first time. She broke off, took Roger in at a single glance, and obviously decided that he was of no importance. 'Good afternoon, Mrs Gale,' she said coldly.

Daphne Gale said as coldly: 'Good afternoon, Lady Foley.'

'Can I help you?'

The Dresden doll of a woman said: 'Not unless you can tell us where to find Syd Cartwright.'

Lionel opened his mouth to speak, but thought better of it. Some kind of secret duel was fought between Gale's wife and the older woman, and it was Lady Foley who came off best, for she said with studied courtesy:

'I will gladly help if I can.'

'Mother,' Lionel said, as if speaking was still an effort, 'the boy's cap was found in the hedge of the drive.'

Lady Foley saw the cap, but didn't speak, and showed no reaction except a kind of surprise. It seemed a long time before she looked at Roger, and asked:

'Are you a policeman?'

'I'm Superintendent West of New Scotland Yard, ma'am, here to try to help to settle this ugly business.'

'I hope you will settle it quickly,' Lady Foley said, and looked away from him to the cap. She did not take much notice of Roger, which might be an unwitting or an intended slight. 'Does that mean you think the boy might be in these grounds?'

'Or the house,' Daphne interpolated.

'Now, Daff!' Her sister was sharp. 'It doesn't prove anything. The cap could have been brought here by someone else, it—' She broke off, as if realizing that she wasn't improving matters.

'What do you wish to do?' Lady Foley decided to accept Roger's presence.

'I'd like to telephone for men to come and help in the search up here,' Roger said promptly. 'The more we can do by daylight the better. May I use your telephone?' He was watching her closely, and knew that she was keenly aware of it. That inattention to him was quite studied; she did not want anyone to think that she was interested in him.

'My son will show you where the telephone is,' she said, and stood aside. Obviously she had no intention of asking the two women in.

Roger stepped ahead of Lionel Foley into a wide hall which would have seemed spacious in any ordinary house, but it stretched a long way and led through an archway into the main hall; he could see the arched windows, churchlike from here, and two or three tall paintings. The floor was of narrow boards, dark with age. He saw a staircase with an ornately carved balustrade, and a minstrels' gallery. All of this he took in at one glance, while Lionel led him into an alcove opposite one of the rectangular windows. The telephone had an oddly naked look; there was a small chair near it and several old telephone directories. Roger called Arncott 51, the number of the emergency line now feeding the Night Shed, and one of Hooper's men answered promptly.

'West here,' Roger said, and could sense the way the Arncott man faced up to the telephone. 'There is a report that the Cartwright boy was seen on the private road approaching Foley Hall. I'd like all searchers to concentrate on the house and grounds, as soon as possible. Will you talk to Mr Hooper?'

'Right away, sir. Any particular approach?'

'I should surround the grounds, and then close in,' said Roger. 'You know the district better than I, and I know you'll make a thorough job of it.'

'We'll see to that, sir!'

Roger put down the receiver. Lionel Foley was staring at him; unexpectedly, he did not look so agitated or so hesitant.

'I suppose that was necessary,' he said.

'Ten minutes could save that lad's life,' Roger responded flatly. 'You won't expect me to stand on ceremony about it. How many servants do you keep here?'

'Three.'

Thirty-three would not have been too many.

'Can they help in the search?'

'I'll fix it,' said Lionel and turned. As he did so, his mother came in, and closed the door behind her; there was a sound of horses moving off. She did not mention Mrs Gale and her sister, but said to Roger:

'What is it you want to see me about, Superintendent?'

'I'd like to clear up some uncertainties about last night,' Roger said, and hesitated for a moment; he felt sure that he knew the best way to handle this woman: 'I expect you know that the rumour that you killed or arranged the killing of Silver Monarch has spread very wide already.'

Lady Foley opened her mouth, really startled; at least she no longer pretended to take no interest in him.

'I didn't expect you to tell me so.'

'Lady Foley, either you know something about the death of the horse and of the stableman, or you don't. If you don't, then we're wasting our time while talking, and the quicker I know the truth the better for you and for us. Will you please tell me where you were last night?'

Lionel broke in: 'Hadn't I better go and help to get things organized?'

'I'm sure the superintendent will allow that,' said Lady Foley.

Roger said: 'I'll see you in a few minutes, sir,' and turned away as if young Foley did not exist. 'Well, Lady Foley?'

'I was here, in this house.'

'All the evening?'

'From yesterday morning until midnight, and I have been here or in the grounds all day today. I seldom go out, I have plenty to do in the house.'

'Did anyone see you here between the hours of nine and eleven o'clock last night?'

'It is unlikely.'

'The servants?'

'I don't ask them to wait on me after eight o'clock, the two house servants are usually up at six o'clock. We live in enlightened times, Superintendent.'

'Some people think so. Was your son here?'

'No. He came from London this morning.'

'Did he blame you for the death of the horse?'

'Had it been his own horse, and had it been killed here, he might have blamed me,' said Lady Foley. 'He might have been justified, too. As it was, it didn't occur to him.'

'Do you know where he stayed last night?'

'Presumably at his club, the Countryman's,' Lady Foley answered. 'You can ask him.'

'Did you go out at all between the hours of nine and eleven o'clock last night?'

'No.'

'If a witness stated that he had seen you in or near the village, what would you say?'

'That he was mistaken or lying.'

'Thank you,' said Roger. He found himself smiling secretly;

and also found himself liking the woman. He wondered how far he could go, and wondered how quickly the county – and the county included the Chief Constable and the Lord Lieutenant – would come to her aid if she found herself under severe pressure. 'Do you know of any enemies in the neighbourhood, Lady Foley?'

'Enemies is a peculiar word to use in the circumstances, isn't it?'

'Do you know of anyone who would wish you harm?'

'No,' she answered flatly. 'I know of a great many who dislike me, but none who bear me active malice – unless it be my son, on certain occasions. He usually repents.' Her lips were smiling, but her eyes were very hard, as if she hated what she was saying.

'The rumours have been taken up with great avidity,' Roger said formally. 'There seems to be malice in the acceptance and malice in the spreading.'

'Mild malice,' she agreed. 'Yes.'

Roger changed the subject without the slightest alteration in his tone.

'I see. How badly did you want the horse Shoestring dead, Lady Foley?'

'Very badly, while it belonged to my son.'

'Why?'

'Hasn't rumour also told you that I believe it would ruin him – as other Foleys have been ruined by their obsession with racehorses?'

'I'm not concerned with that kind of rumour. Is your son in any particular difficulty just now – one likely to make you feel so strongly about his ownership of the horse?'

'If he is, I am not aware of it.'

'Did you employ anyone to go to the stables and attempt to kill the horse?' Roger demanded.

Lady Foley's gaze was very level as she took her time to answer. Then:

'No. I did not leave this house, and I do not employ others to do unpleasant work for me. If you must know, I had intended visiting Mr Gale today in the hope that he would be persuaded to offer my son a reasonable price for his horse. It may gladly live to be a hundred, provided my son doesn't own it.'

'Lady Foley,' Roger said, 'you may have great difficulty in establishing the facts you've stated unless you can name some witness to your statement that you were in the house all last evening.'

'Short of a Peeping Tom, I can't,' she replied, and pressed her hand against her forehead. 'Do you need me any more, Superintendent?'

That was dismissal.

There was nothing Roger could do about it, and nothing that he particularly wanted to. The woman was under great pressure, and withstood it well. Evidence that she had a headache showed in her burning eyes, but she did not look away from him.

'I won't worry you any more than I must,' Roger said. 'Good-day, my lady, and thank—'

The ringing of the telephone bell broke across his words. He was nearer it than Lady Foley, and stretched out a hand for the receiver, then withdrew it as she moved. He wondered if she was a little too anxious to take the call, or whether it was a natural reaction. She announced herself in a cool, detached voice: she would always appear to be cool and dispassionate, no matter how she felt.

'Yes, he's here,' she said and handed Roger the telephone without a word. He took it with a murmured 'Thanks,' and spoke briskly: 'West speaking.'

'Hooper here.' The Arncott man spoke gruffly, but his voice held a note which told Roger he was more excited than he had been, this wasn't a formal call. 'Lady Foley still there?'

'Yes.' She was walking away, very slowly.

'Well, keep her there,' Hooper said. 'I've just been talking to a motorist who saw young Cartwright being driven in her car, towards Foley Hall. That was about half-past eleven this morning, about the time he disappeared. The man knows the car, a big old Austin. Have a look at it as soon as you can, will you? I seem to remember it's got a noisy engine.'

'I'll fix it,' promised Roger, as if this were the least urgent thing imaginable. But his heart was beginning to pound. 'Telephone the Yard for me and ask them to check whether Mr Lionel Foley was at his club, the Countryman's, the night before last, and get all details.'

'Couldn't be in it together, could they?' Hooper demanded.

'We'll see,' Roger said, and rang off. He saw Lady Foley was coming from a doorway on the right; he did not know whether she had heard his request.

'You won't mind if I look round the grounds and the house, if necessary, will you?' he asked.

'You must do whatever you think is your duty,' she said precisely. 'Good afternoon, Superintendent.' She went forward to the door, and seemed glad that he was going; she closed the door on him quite sharply, and he moved away, looking towards the stables and the garage – a converted stable, almost certainly. He could see the tracks made by car tyres, and also the tell-tale drops of oil in the gravel of the drive. He left his own car where it was and walked, not quickly, towards this garage – and then he heard the sound of a car engine, close by.

It had a curiously deep throbbing note.

He expected it to come from the stable yard, but instead, he saw an old, square-looking Austin, black and shining, going in the other direction. He could not see a man at the wheel. The car was being driven too fast, and there were gates on the other side of the stable yard.

He swung round and doubled back to his own car, jumped in, and was on the move within ten seconds. He drove right across the empty stable yard, and when he reached the parkland on the other side, saw the big Austin heading for a thick copse, along a cart-track which was deeply rutted. It was travelling very fast, swaying and rattling, going much faster than was safe.

Roger put his foot down, and chased after it.

He felt sure that Lionel Foley was at the wheel.

CHAPTER VIII

CHASE

THE CAR ahead bounded over a hump of grass, and the wheel swung to the right; for a moment it looked as if it was out of control. Roger saw the wheels swing right and left, then go downwards, at a sharp incline. He was at least a hundred yards away, and there was nothing he could do to stop or to help, but he now recognized Foley in the driving seat.

The old Austin righted itself, then seemed to go faster.

They were in a large paddock, surrounded by once-white rails, all now battered and neglected; a rough kind of track had been cut in the grass, as if for trial gallops. This led from the incline towards a magnificent copse of oak and beech, and the ground was level if bumpy. It was hard to believe that the old car could show such speed, but Foley seemed to know exactly what he was doing.

Roger did not try to think or guess beyond the need for stopping him.

Was he trying to run away?

Roger saw a gap among the trees, and was quite sure that the other driver was heading for it. Now that he was nearer, the copse seemed to spread out in each direction, like a thick wood; the land was much more wooded than had appeared from the road. The Austin seemed to be swallowed up by the trees and the undergrowth. Nothing made sense to Roger, but Foley had been born and had spent his childhood in these grounds, and must know exactly where he was heading: probably to a main road. This was in the general direction of the road, as far as Roger could judge.

The house was out of sight, and Roger was among the trees, following an old cart-track. There was something odd, almost eerie, about driving so fast through the gloom of the woods;

about having the branches of trees loom up and smack against the roof and the side of the car; and hearing the shoots of brambles scratching and screeching along the paint. The car lurched from side to side so much that he had to slow down, although he had not gained much on the Austin. Now and again he caught a glimpse of it through the trees, but for a long period – half a minute seemed in these circumstances long – it was out of sight. The turning of his own engine in third gear and the groaning of the springs as the car lurched, drowned the sound of the car ahead. There were moments when it seemed to Roger that it had got away.

Then he saw a break in the trees, the brightness of full daylight, and a clear sky. The ground seemed less uneven, too, but the Austin wasn't in sight.

As Roger shot the car forward, he saw the land rise sharply on the far side of the trees; beyond there was only open heathland, which seemed to break off, as if the horizon had come forward to greet him. He felt the car slackening speed, but there was a dip in the ground which shot it forward.

Suddenly, he was scared.

He jammed on the brakes, but the grass beneath the wheels was slippery. The car skidded forwards and sideways. That 'horizon' seemed to beckon at him. He turned into a skid, but the car was completely out of control. Its weight and speed carried it a few yards up the slope, and he had a bad moment; an awful glimpse of land stretched out into illimitable distances below. It was as if this was the edge of a cliff, and the land he could see was thousands of feet away.

He could only sit and wait for seconds which seemed agelong.

Then he felt the tyres grip. The wheel responded under his hand, and the car came slowly to a standstill. He could not see the panorama from here, for he was below the level of the cliff. He sat for a moment, cold and sweating, and when he opened the door and got out, his legs were weak. He gripped the side of the door, to steady himself, then went forward. The slope was gentle, here. The view seemed to rise out of nothing, distant at first and filled with a blueish haze. He saw tiny villages and large towns; saw great houses standing on their own, and the needle spires of churches. The criss-cross pattern of fields seemed as sharp and clear as if he were thousands of feet up in an aircraft; and the grey roads wound about the countryside, twisting and turning as if whoever had built them had not known where he was going.

There was a river, too, a flash of silver.

Close to the edge, the slope was much steeper; he had to make an effort to climb. He looked right and left, seeing no trace of the Austin, positive that it had gone over the top, and almost certain now that Lionel Foley had intended to take it there.

Why?

What had terrified him?

Had he learned that his mother's car had been used to carry Syd Cartwright off?

Roger reached the top, and saw the car, hundreds of feet below, lying on its side. One wheel had come off and lay a few yards from the hub. A door had been ripped off, and there was a gaping hole in the roof; but there was no fire. Roger could see where it had gone over the top, at a spot where it was possible to drive for a hundred yards downhill; obviously it had gone out of control where the ground became broken and lumpy, and was dotted with patches of briar and scrub and a few stunted trees. Below the wrecked car the hillside was almost sheer; had it gone another twenty yards it would have fallen out of sight.

There was no sign of Lionel Foley.

*　　　*　　　*

There was no sign of the young man, or of any other living person, only the quietness of the high lands, a quietness which seemed to rise out of the blue haze below.

*　　　*　　　*

Roger looked behind him, and saw nobody. If anyone saw the car they would probably come here, but most would now be concentrating on the search of the grounds, no one was likely to come this far. He could go to fetch help; but if he were gone for half an hour, it might make the difference between life and death if young Foley were injured.

He might still be in the car.

Roger tossed his hat towards his own car, and started down. At first the going was steep but not difficult; then the slope became much steeper, and he had to go very cautiously; he could have done with a stick. He went down sideways, his left foot much lower than his right, because of the sharpness of the incline. Now and again he reached a spot where the ground was much smoother, but most of the time he was swaying right and left, and had to keep touching the ground with his left hand, to steady himself.

He could see no movement inside the car, nothing to suggest that Foley was conscious in there.

Could any man live through such a crash?

The car was now only fifty yards away, and the going was much easier. Roger quickened his pace; but for the slippery grass he could have run. He reached the car and peered into the gaping opening where the door had been.

Foley wasn't inside.

Roger felt mingled relief and disappointment as he peered more intently into the car, looking for details which might tell part of the story. There seemed to be nothing but the shiny brown upholstery, the evidence of an old luxury car, still well kept. There were signs that the leather had recently been washed, though, and a brown smear on one of the foot pedals. He leaned inside and scratched this with his forefinger; underneath the coating, it was crimson.

The smear was of dried blood.

Roger felt excitement surging; it seemed obvious that young Foley had tried but failed to remove all trace of the blood, and tried to destroy the car, hoping it would catch fire. He might have managed to jump from the moving car before it had crashed, or else had been flung clear.

He was not in sight but there was the cliff-like edge fifty yards below. If he had fallen over there, he might have broken his neck.

Fearful of slipping and not quite sure what kind of drop there lay beyond, Roger went forward cautiously. The land gradually opened out in front of him; there was a drop of a hundred feet or more, almost sheer, except that it was broken in places by grassy mounds which looked like rocks over which the grass had grown. The hillside just here was bleak and bare.

Then Roger saw Foley, lying on his side, back towards him. His right leg was bent awkwardly, but there was no outward signs of injury. He lay on one of the mounds; had he been flung ten yards further he would have been over the edge, and almost certainly dashed to his death.

He lay without moving.

Roger said, aloud: 'It's going to be a hell of a climb down.' He hesitated, and looked upwards. From where he was standing he could see the top of the hill, but not his car. No one was in sight. He reminded himself that there was not likely to be anyone for a long time. He wished he had a stick, or anything which would help him to keep upright. He had no taste for the job, but knew that he must go down to Foley; half an hour might save the man's life – and half an hour might give him life enough to make some kind of statement. What compelling urge had driven him to that crazy drive and to this awful risk?

A minute or two would make little difference.

Roger hurried back to the old Austin, and opened the boot; it was not locked. Inside was a coil of rope, but nothing he could use as a walking stick. He took the rope and looped it round his shoulders, then went back. He surveyed the uneven hillside, and saw the best way to get down to the injured man. As he went, he realized how much steeper it was than any land he had climbed before; it was one thing to get down, another to get up. He stopped suddenly, seeing a small bush oak growing almost at a right angle out of the hillside. Slowly, acutely conscious of his precarious foothold, he tied one end of the rope round the base of the tree, and looped the other round his left arm. Holding it loosely, he started down again. The rope ran out before he reached Foley, and he let it go; it would be a help when he climbed up to it again.

Then he saw Foley move his right arm.

He kept quite still, making no noise. A few birds were singing, but until this moment he had not heard them. There was a distant roaring sound, a long way off, but he took no notice of it. Foley moved his arm again, and then his head turned a little, but next moment it dropped back, as if the effort had been too much for him.

Roger started down.

He had to turn his back on Foley, and climb backwards, making sure with each step that the foothold was secure; but Foley lay on a jutting mound, quite flat and safe; and Roger reached him, turned slowly, and looked down.

He was staring up, head twisted round, fear in his eyes.

CHAPTER IX

REASON?

THE HILLSIDE stretched above them, and far below was the broken countryside. Only the birds made any sound, for the roaring had ceased; an aeroplane was now out of sight. The silence seemed to add itself to Foley's fear.

Roger stood over him.

Foley moistened his lips, and said: 'My – my leg feels as if it's broken.'

It might be, but there was no injury to his head, except a bruise or two and a graze on his right cheekbone; and there was no apparent body injury. Roger stood over him, knowing that he looked like a figure of vengeance, the pose over-dramatic; but high drama was exactly what he needed now.

'Why did you do it?'

'I – I don't know. Look at my leg, it's torturing me.'

'It'll be all right when a doctor's seen it, and I'll get you up there as soon as you've told me why you did that.'

'I don't know!'

Foley was sweating; the tell-tale little globules were on his forehead. He was deathly pale too, and that threw up the brilliance and brightness of his grey-blue eyes. His lips were parted, and showed that he had fine, very white teeth. His nostrils were slightly distended, but none of these things altered the fact that he was good-looking in an effeminate kind of way. Oddly, his dark hair curled almost as if it had been artificially waved, and a slight wind stirred it. He wore an old Harris tweed jacket of greeny-grey colour, khaki-coloured breeches and gaiters.

'Don't play the fool,' Roger said. 'You know why you jumped into the car and tried to destroy it – and you know you need a doctor for that leg. The quicker you tell me the one the quicker you'll get the other.'

'You've got to get me a doctor. If you don't I'll make sure—'

He broke off.

Roger bent down, squatting, so that his face was only a yard from Foley's; and Foley must see him still as a kind of figure of vengeance.

'Now don't make any mistake,' Roger said. 'Anything said when we get back will be your word against mine, and mine will be believed. You haven't a chance, so stop stalling; why did you try to destroy that car?'

Foley moistened those feminine lips again.

'I did destroy it.'

'You damaged it. It didn't catch fire – is that what you hoped?'

'Listen, West,' Foley said, in a quivering voice, 'I'm not going to be third-degree'd by you or anyone else. I won't say a word. I've every right to refuse to answer questions, I'm not under arrest.'

'Yet.'

'You can't bluff me and you can't frighten me,' Foley said, and wiped his hand across his forehead, to brush off that sweat of fear. 'You're just wasting your time. Go and get me a doctor.'

Roger said, very slowly: 'I once had to wait forty-eight hours with a man who wouldn't talk. I didn't enjoy being without food and drink for as long as that, but it was worth it; he talked in the end.' He took out cigarettes, lit one and flicked the match away; he noticed Foley's intake of breath, as if the man longed to draw in the smoke, too. The pallor and the sweat were still there, and so was the fear; but there was a lot more courage in Lionel Foley than his looks suggested.

He insisted: 'I'm not going to say a word,' and turned and stared out over the panorama which was so calm and beautiful.

He could really get tough, Roger thought grimly; he could

show a hardness which might frighten a man or boy into thinking he would be as hard as rock, but he could no more let the man lie there with that injured leg than he could have broken the leg himself; but he did not have to say so. He shifted his position a little and drew deeply on the cigarette, blew smoke close to Foley's face, and said:

'Let me have a look at that leg.'

'Only a doctor—'

'Let me have a look and don't be a fool!' Roger moved again and felt the leg above the knee; there was nothing the matter with it. He unfastened the gaiter, and then prodded gently; Foley winced, but there was no sign of a fracture. Roger took off the boot, unlacing it to its fullest extent. The ankle was already swollen, and might be very painful, but there seemed no serious fracture. He pressed and moved the ankle a little; Foley drew in a hissing breath.

Roger let the leg rest gently on the ground.

'That's a sprain. You don't need a doctor, you need a cold compress.' He stood up. 'What chance do you think there is of us being found here?'

'How do I know?'

'Listen to me, Foley,' said Roger, inwardly fuming, but outwardly as calm as a man could be. If he could make this man talk now it might enable him to find the missing boy, who was all-important. He must take a chance, and try to panic Foley into talking; a kind of psychological third-degree. Foley might pull strings afterwards to get him sharply reprimanded: but only the truth mattered now, no matter how rough he had to sound.

'I could go back, and get lost,' he threatened. 'I could go back and forget that I'd been here. I could leave you lying here until it gets dark, and I doubt whether any search party would venture down here. Don't underrate me.'

'What the hell gives you the right to behave like this?'

'Two Cartwrights,' Roger answered. 'One battered to death

and the other missing – with his cap found close to your home. *Where is he?*'

'Don't ask me, I don't know!'

'You know. Where's young Syd?'

'I tell you I don't know.'

'You know. If you've killed him—'

'I haven't killed him, I haven't killed anybody.'

'I think you're lying.' Roger squatted down again, and his face very close to the other man's. He could see the alarm in those blue-grey eyes, could see the way the mouth went slack. Yet there was far greater toughness than he had suspected in the man. 'You're lying and I know it. You drove that car with the child in it. He threw his cap out of the window, and you didn't know it. You tried to set fire to the car and destroy the bloodstains. Come on, out with it, admit it.'

'It's not true!'

'It's so true any jury will convict you.'

'I tell you it's not true!'

'Listen to me, you murdering swine, I could choke the life out of you.' Roger actually crooked his fingers close to Foley's neck. 'The boy was in the car, and you meant to destroy the evidence. *Where is he?*'

'I don't know where he is!'

'*Where is he?*'

'Get away from me,' Foley gasped, and he tried to move, and actually strike at Roger's hands. 'You're lying, I didn't see him, I only saw—'

He broke off.

'Make it quick,' Roger said. 'Make it convincing enough for a jury, but there's a lot of evidence against you.' There were the bloodstains in the car, evidence which might damn this man, there was never likely to be another chance like this of making Foley talk.

'I only saw the cap being thrown out of the car,' Foley said, and closed his eyes, as if he could not bear to keep them open now that he had given up. 'I was in the field. I heard the car and I thought it was – was my mother. I saw someone throw the cap out of the window and it caught in the hedge. I didn't think any more about it. The gardener uses the car sometimes to take his sister's children to and from school. I thought—'

He broke off.

Roger said, more quietly: 'Go on.'

'I thought one of the kids was playing the fool, that's all. It wasn't until Mrs Gale brought the cap in and said that it was Syd Cartwright's that I realized what it meant.'

'What did it mean?'

Foley opened his eyes.

'I hate the sight of you,' he said carefully. 'I'll make sure everyone knows how you behaved, you'll never live this down.'

'What did it mean?' repeated Roger.

'You know as well as I do. If my mother's car had been used—' He broke off, and pressed his hands against his eyes. 'Oh, I'm so worked up I hardly know what to think. Why don't you do some of the thinking for a change? I – I've been living on my nerves for a week, I hardly slept a wink last night, I hardly know what I'm doing.'

'Did you know you were killing Syd Cartwright?'

Foley didn't respond at once, but let his head rest on the ground. There was a kind of peace in his expression now, as if by talking as much as he had, he had greatly eased the burden of his fear. When he spoke, it was very quietly.

'I didn't kill or kidnap anyone, West, and you know it. I may have been crazy to want to get rid of the car so that you couldn't tell it had been used, but there were bloodstains in it. I washed them off, but some were left, and when I saw you I realized that I had to destroy the stains somehow. It was a kind of panic.'

'And what made you so quixotic?' Roger demanded stonily.

'I owe her something.'

'Your mother?'

'Of course I mean my mother. Do you want it all in words of three letters?'

Roger said: 'No.' He put his hand to his hip pocket and drew out a leather brandy flask, unscrewed the cap, and handed the flask to Foley. 'Have a nip.' Foley looked astonished at this change of mood, sipped, and wiped the mouth of the flask with his left hand.

'Thanks.'

'Cigarette?'

'Please. I've run out.'

Roger gave him a cigarette, and lit it.

'Now let's spend five minutes putting this in its right perspective before we tackle the job of getting you up to the top,' he said. 'You saw the cap being flung out, and jumped to the conclusion that it was the cap which Mrs Gale found. Right?'

'Of course it was the same cap.'

'Probably. You suspected that your mother's car had been used when Syd had been kidnapped. Is that what you're saying?'

'It's obvious, isn't it?'

'Did you see who was driving?'

'No.'

'Was it a man or woman?'

'I didn't see who was driving.'

'You say the gardener often uses the car.'

'Yes,' Foley said, 'and I thought he was driving as I told you, but when I came back to the house I knew it hadn't been him. He had been working in the garden or the greenhouses all the morning. The maid told me.'

'Thanks. Is there only one gardener?'

'There are two, but only one's fully effective. That's George Ansell. His father still works, but is nearly past it.'

'What's this about a sister's children?'

Foley answered: 'If it matters, George Ansell and his father live at a cottage with George's widowed sister and her children. The sister is a part-time maid at the Hall.'

'Where is Colonel Madden's cottage?'

'Near the kitchen garden,' Foley answered.

'How much blood was there in the car?' Roger demanded sharply.

'Listen, West, you've made me say a lot more than I meant to,' Foley said. 'I'm not going to say anything else. You can leave me here all night if you like, but you won't get another word out of me. I shouldn't leave me here though. People are inclined to believe a Foley against everyone else in this part of the world. If you'll help me up, I think I can hobble to the top.'

The brandy had strengthened his nerve; giving him that might have been a mistake, but there was no real need to have the i's dotted and the t's crossed. The story was plausible, the bloodstains provided the evidence needed – and also gave reason to fear that young Syd might be dead.

Roger stood up, and looked about him, to make sure which was the best way back, and then braced himself to help Foley to his feet. The man's left ankle was much more swollen, and there was no hope of getting his boot on again. Roger slung it round his neck, by the laces, and Foley put his left arm round his shoulder. Together, they started back, slowly at first. When they reached the rope both of them were able to pull on it, and it was surprisingly easy, if very slow. It would take at least half an hour to reach the top, and ten minutes to get from here to the first brow, and to the hillside where the Austin lay on its side.

There was the noise of their heavy breathing; the noise of the birds; and another sound, like a roaring, which Roger heard but could not place. He did not think much about it. He was sweating, and could tell that Foley was in more pain than he had expected; he kept touching the ground with his injured foot, that was probably the cause. He was sweating, too, and although he was so thin, his willowy height made him weigh at least eleven stone; he leaned most of that weight on Roger.

'What's that noise?' he asked suddenly.

'The roaring?'

'Yes.'

'I've been wondering,' Roger said.

'It sounds like a fire.'

'Do you have heath fires at this time of the year?'

'There shouldn't be any this year, we've had too much spring rain.'

Roger looked up, and said: 'Well, it is a fire.' A cloud of smoke was drifting over their heads, and he felt a townsman's moment of alarm, for he did not know the possible extent and ferocity of a heath fire near here. There had been no sign of smoke when he had come down.

Heath fire be damned!

He snapped: 'Rest here!' and eased Foley down to the ground, then started up the hillside as fast as he could, scrambling much of the way on all fours, peering at the smoke all the time. He could smell it now, and knew that it came from no heath fire; petrol was burning.

He saw over the brow.

The car was a blazing mass, the roar was coming from it, and smoke was billowing up, dense and black just above the car but thinning out in the wind. A long way off, near the brow of the hill, was a solitary horseman; it was impossible to tell if it were man or woman. The horse and rider seemed to breast the top of the hill as Roger watched, and a moment later, disappeared.

He could feel the heat of the fire, and knew that nothing could put it out.

*   *   *

Who else wanted to destroy any evidence which the car might offer?

Lady Foley?

As he watched it blaze, Roger felt a tension greater than he had yet known here. At first, this had been simply a case to investigate with all the expertise he possessed. It had been more interesting than most, because of the background and because of the people. The disappearance of the murdered man's son had given a touch of urgency, forcing him to accept the ruthlessness of whoever was committing the crimes; and he thought of the word 'ruthless' as he stared at the fire which destroyed the bloodstains beyond all reasonable hope of identification.

There was only his word that any had been there, and that would be useless in a charge.

Foley called: 'What is it?'

'Someone finished your job for you,' Roger said roughly, and turned round.

'What do you mean?' Foley demanded.

'The car's burning.'

'You mean someone set fire to it?' Foley's eyes lit up.

'That's what I mean.'

'But – but that's impossible! Couldn't – couldn't there have been a delayed-action fire?'

'The petrol tank didn't burst, there was no leakage that I could see,' Roger said. 'Who would you expect to want to destroy it?'

'It's no use asking me.'

'I am asking you,' Roger said, 'and don't start stalling again.'

Foley said: 'I've told you that I'm not going to say another word, and that stands.'

The unmistakable fact was that he looked puzzled.

Roger reached him, and they started the climb again. Soon Foley would be able to hobble with much less help. As he supported him, Roger kept seeing that yellowy-red fire in his mind's eyes, and seeing the solitary horseman or horsewoman. But superimposed upon these things was the harsh fact of this ruthlessness; and with it came the realization that the stable lad Syd was still missing.

Did Foley know where he was?

Was he alive?

They dragged themselves over the top of the first brow. The fire was burning low now, and the smoke had faded a great deal, but as they went near the red-hot wreck of twisted metal, the wind carried the heat to them. They gave the car a wide berth, and started towards the top of the hill again. As they passed the car, Roger saw two riders appear; then several more. The riders put their horses towards the car and the two climbers.

One rider was Daphne Gale; another was Jenkins; Roger recognized a heavy, rotund man as Colonel Madden, whose photograph was often in the shiny weeklies. Just ahead of Madden was Lady Foley. She was in dark brown riding breeches and wearing a riding hat, looking as if she had been born to the saddle, too.

She stared at the fire, and then at her son.

Daphne Gale said, with a catch in her voice: 'Syd wasn't in that car, was he?'

'No,' Roger assured her, and felt his heart sink with the sharp reminder of the possible significance of the blood stains. But he asked briskly: 'Did you all ride together?'

'No, we rode from the road with Mrs Gale and her sister,' Colonel Madden answered. 'Saw the smoke. Lady Foley came from the house. Eh, Martha?'

So Lady Foley could have been the lone rider.

CHAPTER X

QUICK GLIMPSE

IF ANY of them realized the significance of the question, nothing was said, but the glance between Lady Foley and Daphne Gale was sharp and hostile. Gale's wife found it more difficult to hide her hostility than the older woman.

Lady Foley said: 'Are you badly hurt, Lionel?'

'Twisted my ankle, and it feels like a balloon,' young Foley muttered. 'I'll be all right when I've had a cold compress on it.'

'It will have to be X-rayed,' Roger said. 'We'll get it done as soon as we can get him into Arncott.'

Jenkins was already standing by Foley's side, and a stable lad on the other side. Between them, with comparatively little effort, they hoisted Lionel Foley to the saddle of a horse; the stable lad mounted behind. Roger could ride with Jenkins, or walk; and haste was more important than dignity. He had to be helped up, but found the saddle surprisingly comfortable. It was five years since he had ridden a horse – during a procession in London – and he had never climbed up a steep hill on horseback. But with the stableman behind it was unexpectedly easy, and Roger was glad to take his weight off his legs. Now that the immediate crisis was over, he felt a reaction almost of exhaustion.

Soon they were at the top. Three or four other riders were gathered there, staring down at the still smouldering wreckage, but the sight which most pleased Roger was Snell, near a Vespa motor-scooter propped up on its stand.

'Anything I can do, sir?' he asked promptly. The 'sir' was for Lady Foley's benefit.

'Yes, Inspector. I'll send some men here as soon as I can. Meanwhile I don't want anyone to go down to the car, or over the brow at all. I want to get several sets of hoofprints, so that we can find out exactly who's been down there, and—'

Lady Foley was smiling for the first time; Foley actually grinned. Daphne Gale gave a little gesture which suggested that she was prepared for any kind of idiocy. Snell kept a commendably straight face as he spoke, and even his eyes forebore to grin.

'Not likely to find many prints on grass, sir.'

'There are bare patches of earth near the car, and there is a path,' Roger said coldly. 'One hoofprint might be enough to identify our man. Help Mr Foley into the back of my car, will you? And make sure no one goes down there.'

'Very good, sir.' Snell appeared duly humbled.

Lady Foley was still smiling faintly, but Daphne Gale looked at Roger as if with new interest. She was too tense all the time; Roger had an impression that her mind and her mood was as brittle as the china which she seemed to be made of. He wanted a talk with her, and wanted to find out the reason for the open hostility towards Lady Foley, but there were other more urgent questions. It was always the same; sooner or later he was pitchforked into a situation where half a dozen things needed doing at once. There was a kind of driving urgency in him, the moment he began an investigation, and now the cause of the compulsion was the missing stable lad.

Jenkins had helped Lionel Foley into the car. Foley sat in one corner with his legs stuck right out in front of him, and did not look at anyone. His mother was eyeing him, as if she could not understand his aloofness. Roger went round to the other side, and took the wheel. There was a curious kind of silence as he started off. He found himself wondering where Mrs Gale's sister Kathleen had gone, and couldn't remember her surname; that detail annoyed him. He drove slowly across the uneven land, knowing that he was jolting the injured man badly. By looking to the right he could see Foley's face, tight-lipped, as if the ankle was really hurting him. Foley was leaning back with his eyes closed and it was difficult to assess his expression.

Roger asked sharply: 'You're quite sure that your mother is involved, aren't you?'

Foley didn't answer.

'Aren't you, Foley?'

'The only thing I'm sure of is that I'm not going to say another word until I have legal advice,' Foley said. 'Is there anything criminal in that precaution?'

Roger answered in a harsh, clipped voice.

'There's plenty of folly but no crime. Did you ever pause to think what kind of job we police have to do? We can call on every kind of expert we want. We can get the best possible advice from experts in horses and riding. We can smother the whole of this neighbourhood with men, all of them asking questions. We're going to have to find out who drove that car this morning, and we're going to ask everyone in the village, if necessary everyone in the surrounding villages, perhaps as far away as Reading. We could put it out on radio and television – I've only to say the word. We're certainly going to ask for a statement from anyone who was seen driving your mother's car, and nine out of ten of them are going to jump to the conclusion that she's involved.'

Foley growled: 'Well, don't you think she is?'

'You seem to think she is, that's all. If you tell us why, I can sift the facts. That's my job. But I can't sift them until I know them. More people have been in trouble and fallen under suspicion because well-meaning fools have withheld vital facts. Once I know why you're so sure about your mother, I can find out whether you're right or not.'

'Very plausible, but I'll talk when I've seen a lawyer,' Foley sneered. 'You're wasting your time.'

Roger said: 'Make sure you're not making a lot of trouble for yourself and your mother.'

Foley didn't respond.

Roger drove through the stable yard, the way he had come,

and then towards the Hall. He saw a chestnut horse which he thought was familiar standing in a small paddock. As he approached the side of the house, Daphne Gale's sister came round the corner from the front entrance, walking; she looked strikingly lovely, with her auburn hair falling to her shoulders, wearing a close fitting shirt and jodhpurs; Kathleen What-was-her-name? She was flicking a small whip against her leg as she came hurrying, and Roger pulled up.

'Can I help you?'

'My horse has gone lame,' she said. 'I feel so useless standing about here. Can you take me back to Arncott Stables?'

'Of course.' Roger started to open his door.

'Don't get out,' she insisted, and opened the door next to him, then saw Lionel Foley, with his leg stuck out and his boot off. 'Oh!' She hesitated, half in and half out of the car. 'I didn't see you, Mr Foley.'

'Hallo, Miss Russell.' How could one forget a name as ordinary as that? There was a brighter note in Foley's voice. 'Don't worry about me. I wrenched my ankle, and Mr West's taking me to hospital for an X-ray.'

'I *am* sorry.'

'My own clumsy fault,' Foley said.

Kathleen Russell closed the door, and sat so that she could see and talk to Foley. Roger sensed a kind of tension between them, although tension wasn't quite the right word. Both Foley and the girl seemed glad to have been thrown together. There was a certain restrained eagerness in the way they talked, and although they discussed the missing boy, there was no feeling in their voices; their interest for the moment was almost entirely in themselves.

Callous?

Roger thought: 'Nonsense,' and drove steadily down to the stables. A uniformed policeman was on duty outside, and there were signs of activity inside; horses could not be neglected, even for the search. The girl got out before Roger could open his door.

'Thank you very much . . .'

When they drove on, Foley was silent. Roger saw him in the mirror; his eyes were wide open, there was eagerness in his expression, a glint in his eyes which hadn't been there before. Yet everything the couple had said and everything he had heard made it almost certain that they were strangers.

Were they?

Roger wondered when the Yard's report on Foley at the Countryman's Club would arrive.

Arncott Cottage Hospital was just on the far side of the town. Roger took Foley there, promised to send a taxi for him, and drove immediately to police headquarters, which were in a side street almost in the middle of the little town, with its low, timbered buildings, some of them thatched, and with the Tudor market hall in the middle of the wide High Street. It was as if a piece of Tudor England had been left untouched through the centuries. Very few people were about, although all the shops were open. Roger turned left, and saw the police station. It was a new, starkly modern building, standing back from the side road and with plenty of parking room in a courtyard at the front. He pulled up near the steps and hurried out; and as he reached the top, Hooper came hurrying down stairs which Roger could see through the wide, glass swing doors.

Roger stepped into a spacious, bare hall, with the figure of Justice, with her scales and sword, in mosaic on the floor and on the walls. Black-painted doors were marked: *Charge Room. CID Waiting Room. Inquiries.* The stairs were of a cold pale grey stone. Against this background Hooper looked even more burly.

He was grinning.

'I got news,' he announced.

'You surprise me,' said Roger, but failed to hide his eagerness. 'Have you found . . .'

'Not so good as that,' said Hooper, and disappointment flashed into those veined eyes. 'But I've two witnesses who caught a glimpse of the car about eleven-fifteen this morning.

It was turning off the road into the lane which leads to Foley House. Guess who was driving.'

He could be schoolboyish.

Roger said: 'If I had to guess, I'd say Lady Foley.'

'Right in one,' boomed Hooper. 'I should say we've almost enough on her to pull her in. Wouldn't like to yet. I've had a word from the Chief Constable. Apparently all the hoary skeletons of aristocracy are rallying round the lady, so I'd better not put a foot wrong. But this is one of those cases where the obvious thing is the right one.'

Roger rubbed the back of his head.

'I wish it weren't quite so obvious,' he remarked. 'You changed your mind?'

'About what?'

'Lady Foley not battering Ted Cartwright.'

'I said she might have hired someone else,' Hooper reminded him, 'and if that someone was recognized and killed Ted, her nibs would be in so deep that she would have to do all she could to cover up.'

'Such as kidnapping and killing the younger man?'

'Listen, Handsome,' Hooper protested, 'I said we had to make sure that we didn't put a foot wrong, but here are some facts. Lady Foley's car was seen in the village last night, just after half past ten. No one saw who was driving, but it was her car all right. It had the noise Syd described, too. It was seen again on the road over the heath this morning, when young Cartwright was last seen galloping. Later, the car was seen moving along the private road to the house, and Syd's cap was found in the hedge. Lady F. was the driver. We've got to get the timing right, but that's the only reasonable doubt.' There was a dogged note in his voice. 'I think that she hired—'

'Hired?'

'Handsome, what's on your mind?' Hooper demanded, almost exasperatedly.

'Let's go to your office,' Roger said, and Hooper led the

way up the cold, almost repellent stairs, to a wide landing with more black-painted doors with names and notices on them in white. There were Detective Inspectors, Detective Officers, Uniformed Branch, CID, Chief Constable; and there were the names of several Chief Inspectors, including Hooper. A wide passage led to the various departments, of photography and fingerprints and records; this was a big town police headquarters in miniature.

Hooper's office was small, square, and immaculate; there was not a loose paper on his large desk, nor on the desk of an elderly man in plain clothes who jumped up. Nothing here was like Hooper the Uncouth.

'Siddown, Sergeant,' Hooper grunted. 'This is Superintendent West – Sergeant Dayton. Anything in from the Yard about young Foley in London?'

'No, sir.'

'Give 'em another hour, and then wake 'em up. These Yard blokes.' Hooper kept a straight face. 'Now go and check that stuff in the photography room.'

When the man had gone and Roger was sitting in a contemporary armchair, Hooper took out cigarettes and pushed them across his shiny, imitation-wood desk. 'What *is* on your mind?' he demanded. 'Don't tell me you took one look at Lady F. and decided that she couldn't be the murderer.'

Roger grinned. 'I don't come to conclusions like that until the second meeting,' he said. 'Hoop, everything you say squares. Are these witnesses absolutely reliable?'

'A local butcher's vanman, and a lad from the Arncott Stables, chap named Tree. Sly type, but he wouldn't make that kind of mistake. Both men of middle age, both of them been most of their lives in Arncott. They saw her driving the car all right.'

'They see the Cartwright boy?'

'No, but they know the time they were out near the Hall, and when we've checked the time Syd was seen, I think we'll find that the timing is right. I've a kind of timetable here,'

Hooper added, opening a manilla folder and pushing a sheet of paper across to Roger. 'See how it works out?'

Roger studied it. Here was the time when Syd had taken the grey horse out, the time that he had been seen on the heath, the time he had been seen galloping after the car. Pencilled in, with query marks beside them, were estimated times when the car had been seen heading for Foley House with Lady Foley at the wheel. There was another inked-in time, 12.04, showing when a local telephone operator had spoken to Lady Foley herself at the house.

'And if she was there at that time, she didn't have long to move about,' said Hooper. 'Fits, doesn't it?'

'If we can ink in those pencilled times, we could have her in for questioning,' Roger agreed. 'And it squares with young Foley's behaviour.'

He explained briefly.

Hooper sat back, rubbing his big hands.

'I don't know what more you want. Young Foley knew his mother was driving that car, and knew Syd Cartwright was in it. Blood being thicker than water, he decided that he had to try to cover up, and destroy the car to make sure we couldn't prove anything. Right?'

'Obvious.'

'Well?'

'And it stinks,' Roger said.

'Now, come.'

'It makes Lady Foley a fool. She isn't.'

'I don't follow you.'

'Only a fool would have shown herself driving that car with the boy in it.'

'She might not have had any choice.'

'I know that one,' Roger said. 'It's the old story – that she put someone up to going down to kill Shoestring. Whoever it was made a mistake, and went too far, and so she was involved.'

'You're quoting me,' Hooper said.

'It still makes her a fool. If she is a wise woman, and she is, once this misfired she would come and admit it. She would say she had not instructed murder, which was entirely the responsibility of the killer. She had everything to gain and nothing to lose by coming clean. Then there's another thing. Who would she hire to carry out the killing of the horse? You've said that she would do her own dirty work, and I think I agree – she would rather do it than pay anyone else. But supposing she did pay someone? She was putting herself into the hands of the people whom she employed. What's more, they were taking a great risk – if they were caught, they would undoubtedly go to prison. I simply can't see Lady Foley employing a couple of people with that kind of mentality. She couldn't afford it; couldn't afford to take the risk of being implicated, and of being blackmailed.'

Hooper said slowly: 'All right, but there's one thing you've overlooked.'

Roger hoped it was the one thing he had omitted – the chance he was giving Hooper to improve on a Yard man's reasoning: that Lady Foley might have employed a relation.

'What's the one thing?' Roger asked.

'That she's Lady Foley.'

'Come again.'

'As Lady Foley she might be able to call on people who were absolutely reliable.'

'Ah! Such as?'

'Colonel Madden, who's always hard up,' Hooper said, and fully justified himself. 'The old gardener, Ansell, and his son.'

Roger said, just as slowly: 'You might talk me into this. I haven't seen them yet.'

'Old Ansell has worked at Foley Park for nearly sixty years. He started there as a boy of twelve,' said Hooper. 'He's nearly past it. His son's worked there for thirty-five years. They're the old family retainer type, even if you London chaps think the race is extinct, and they've never mixed well with the horsey kind. I can remember a time when there was a kind of war at the Hall between the Ansells and the gardeners they used to have under them, and the stable lads and grooms. That's only fifteen or twenty years ago. The gardeners were put off one by one, until only the Ansells were left, but the grooms and stable lads were kept on for years afterwards. Old Lord Foley would give up anything and sacrifice anything for his precious horse-racing. So you've a history of dislike if not of hatred.'

Roger said slowly: 'You're selling me the idea. What are the Ansells like?'

'They're a surly pair, and they keep themselves to themselves. Live with a widowed daughter and her kids. George Ansell won't have anything to do with any of the Arncott girls — not much with Arncott, either. They do their shopping in Reading on market days, never get a thing they can avoid buying in Arncott.'

'Checked where they were last night?'

'I'm checking,' Hooper assured him.

Roger lit one of the cigarettes, at last, and grinned in such a way that Hooper looked at him suspiciously.

'No, I'm not making this up,' he said. 'And the Ansells would want to make sure that we couldn't get any dope on them from that car, wouldn't they?'

'What kind of dope?'

'Fingerprints, or—'

'But they know that everyone knows they'd be likely to use the car, even if only for cleaning. And George Ansell drives it sometimes — you told me so. The one thing we know for certain is that young Foley was prepared to take great risks to destroy the car, and that someone else, a good horseman or horsewoman, made a job of it,' Roger went on. 'Can the Ansells ride?'

'Handsome,' Hooper said, 'if the Ansells were involved, if they killed Cartwright, Lady Foley would feel under an obligation to keep quiet and so help them. If she put them up to it in the first place, the obligation would be that much the greater. Agreed about that?'

'You could be right,' Roger conceded. 'Any history of bad blood between the Ansells and the Cartwrights?'

Hooper didn't answer.

Roger said: 'Don't make any up, either.'

'No, I won't make anything up,' Hooper said, in a taut voice. He pressed a bell which was set at the side of his desk, and sat back, obviously taken by an idea which seemed of startling importance. After a moment, Sergeant Dayton came in. 'Sergeant,' Hooper demanded at once, 'how long have you lived in Arncott?'

'All my life, sir. I was a constable down at Foley when I first began.'

'Thirty years ago?'

'Thirty-two years,' the elderly sergeant claimed, with obvious and honest pride.

'Didn't the Cartwrights get involved in some kind of scandal, twenty-five years or so ago?'

'That they did,' affirmed Dayton. 'Ted Cartwright's wife died, and he was always one for his bed-life, usually had a little outside interest, as you might say. After he was widowed he was quite a lad, until he was copped with his trousers down, as you might say, with the wife of the gardener at Foley House.'

'Who was the gardener?'

'Jake Ansell, of course,' Dayton answered, and when neither of the others spoke, he went on: 'There was never much love lost between the Ansells and the horsey staff, and after that you could say there was hatred. It was all smoothed over, of course, and Jake's wife stayed on at the Hall as a kind of cook-general. But she died a few years afterwards – I've heard it said that Jake never took her to bed with him again.'

Hooper began to rub his hands together.

'Get that written down in the form of a report, and find at least two other men, on the force or retired, who can vouch for it,' he ordered. 'I'd like it by six o'clock.' He nodded dismissal, and before the door closed on the sergeant, went on: 'It's beginning to take shape. The Ansells would know that the Cartwrights were on duty last night. I wouldn't put it past them to have killed Silver Monarch first because they knew that it was Ted Cartwright's pride. They were given an opportunity at last, and took it. Lady F. would stand by them all right.'

'Could be,' Roger agreed, very thoughtfully. 'The sooner I talk to the Ansells the better.'

'I'll fix it,' Hooper said, and put a hand on the telephone; it rang almost as he touched it. He plucked it up, and announced: 'Hooper .. Who? ... What?' He bellowed that word, and flashed at Roger: 'They think they've found Syd Cartwright's body,' and then listened intently at the telephone.

CHAPTER XI

SECOND BODY

DETECTIVE INSPECTOR SNELL, who had been so prompt to hire a motor-scooter, really knew this district well, and he had primed himself with up-to-date information plus a little gossip. He had a deep and exhaustive knowledge of his job and duties, and carried out Roger's instructions precisely. He did not leave the spot overlooking the burned-out car until several Arncott policemen had arrived, with detailed orders. Then Snell went back to the house, his long legs straddling the small machine, which bounced over the uneven ground. He looked about him – first at the paddock, which was a wreck of its old glory, then at the stables, which had once been nearly as big as the stables down at the village, and then at the vegetable garden. This was near the stables, and separated from the Hall itself by a high brick wall.

Snell went up to a gate which was just wide enough to take a farm cart, and stared at the garden. In one corner was a pigsty, and in another, a fowl run; Foley Hall was self-supporting in most dairy and market-garden foods. He took little interest in pigs or fowls, but watched young George Ansell – still 'young' at forty-nine – digging a long patch of earth, which looked rich and black. Ansell looked up but took no notice of him.

Old Jake came in through a narrow gate on the other side, pushing a wheelbarrow. If he saw Snell, he showed no sign. He went to another corner of the garden, and began to spread the manure; both father and son worked with slow, deliberate movements which disguised the fact that they got through a great deal of work.

Snell climbed off his machine, leaned it against the wall,

and walked in. George did not look up as the detective arrived, but he spoke.

'What are you after?'

'Syd Cartwright,' Snell said. 'Seen him?'

'Ain't seen no one.' Young Ansell went on digging.

'Why aren't you out searching?'

'Can't you see I'm busy?'

'We asked everyone to drop what he was doing and join in the search. It might make the difference between life and death.'

'None of my business,' young Ansell said. 'We've got enough work for four men, we can't find time to stop and help the police.'

'So I see,' Snell said nastily. 'How much of this land have you turned over today?'

'All of it.'

'What's going in there?'

'Early peas and broad beans,' the gardener answered. 'What business is it of yours?'

'My business is to find Syd Cartwright, and if he's dead he's probably buried,' Snell said, with brutal directness. 'Newly-turned soil is an easy place to dig in a quick hole, isn't it?'

George Ansell stopped digging for the first time, and swung round. He was using a fork; the sharp, bright points glistening in the sun, and he held it rather like a rifle with the bayonet fixed.

'If you're accusing me—'

'I'm not accusing anybody.' Snell hid his satisfaction at having worried the man. 'But I want to see that soil turned over again, pretty quick.'

George glowered: 'It'll take more than you to make me turn a spade of it,' he growled. 'If you want it done, you'll have to ask her ladyship.'

'Got something to hide, Ansell?'

'I've work to do and no time to waste,' the gardener

retorted roughly, 'and I don't take orders from anyone but her ladyship.'

Snell said: 'It would take you ten minutes to dig it over, no more.'

'It won't take me two, unless her ladyship gives the word.'

Snell said: 'Right.' He swung back to the gate and his Vespa, and called out as if someone else was near: 'Keep an eye on the kitchen garden, will you, I'll be back.' He started off his engine with a sharp kick, and roared away. No one else was near, now, but the side door of the great house was open. He rang the bell. At one time the door would have been opened by a flunkey; now, Lady Foley came along briskly, still dressed for riding, still looking youthful and full of vigour.

'Sorry to worry you, my lady,' Snell said, with just the right tone of humility, 'but I've a little problem you could help me with.'

'Yes?' She gave him no encouragement.

'I've been ordered to check all recently dug ground, my lady, and there's a large patch in your kitchen garden. The Ansells won't turn it over for me to see without orders from you.'

'I should hope not,' she said. 'What do you expect to find under it?'

'Good manure down to a spit and a spit and a half, if I know good gardeners when I see them,' Snell answered.

There was a slight relaxing in the woman's manner, and she said: 'I'll give you a note. Wait here, please.' She went off, turning into a room on the right, and leaving the door wide open. Snell looked about him, seeing the way the place had gone to seed, wondering what life was like here at normal times. If the woman had any sense, she would sell the place and buy a cottage where she could manage for herself.

She came back with the note.

Snell touched his forehead.

'Thank you, my lady.' He went off, meek until she was

out of sight, and grinning the moment he felt that she had gone.

In the kitchen garden he found father and son talking together, near the newly-dug earth. They were very much alike, but it would have surprised no one had the old man been nearer eighty than seventy. His son was a little taller, and a little broader, and both looked sturdy and hardy.

Snell handed Old Jake the note. He opened it and pretended to read, although he was known to be hopelessly short-sighted. Then he nodded, and George said gruffly:

'If I had my way, you'd do all the digging yourself.'

'Lend me a fork,' Snell said briskly, 'and I'll dig as fast as you.'

George didn't speak. Old Jake stalked off, to watch, obviously determined that nothing would make him help. George fetched a fork for Snell, who turned up the bottoms of his trousers and began to dig as he was wont to do in his own back garden. It was not the first time he had dug in the hope or the fear of finding a body. He rammed the fork down into the thick, loose soil, twisted, pulled it out again, and jabbed. George was much slower and more thorough; as if he wanted to turn every spit over before being sure that it was just plain soil.

Each started from an end of the twenty-yards line; after five minutes, they were each a quarter of the way towards the middle, and the sound of the forks and their movements were remarkably rhythmic. Snell was beginning to sweat, and wished that he had not started off so quickly; but nothing would make him slacken his speed now. He had come to the conclusion that young George was too uninterested to be worried, and he did not seriously expect to find anything here.

His fork went into a different kind of substance, and when he turned it, it would not move so easily. He tried again, and still met resistance. George was plodding along, looking down at the soil itself, and apparently oblivious of Snell, his father, and the billowing clouds which now covered most of the sky.

Snell drew the fork upwards; it did not come easily.

He gulped.

He jabbed the fork in more cautiously next time, a little way from the difficult spot, and tossed the heavy earth on one side. Then he began to make a small hole, getting nearer to the tough spot with every movement.

A red tinge on the prongs of the fork first told him what he had discovered.

*   *   *

News that Syd's body had been found travelled fast, and as Roger drove up the private drive leading to Foley Hall, a dozen or more villagers were walking across the parkland towards the gardens. It was getting dark. Two cyclists jumped quickly off their bicycles as the two cars passed. Snell was now sitting beside Roger; he had said very little since Roger had met him at the police station.

Hooper, who drove in the first car, seemed to be determined to tear the guts out of his engine; there was something savage in the way he swung his wheel round the bends. When he jammed on his brakes when a woman and two children appeared just round a corner, Roger saw the terror in the woman's face. She was heading for the house.

Hooper stopped. Roger saw the woman, a middle-aged, rather pleasant, plumpish type, with a child of eight or nine holding one hand, and a younger one holding the other, pressed against the hedge.

'Where are you going?' Hooper demanded in a voice which travelled clearly.

'I'm going home,' the woman said, and her fear had gone. 'Is it true that they've found Syd Cartwright in the kitchen garden up at the Hall?'

'Yes,' Hooper answered roughly.

The woman closed her eyes, and for a moment, it looked as if she would faint. One child, a boy, stared at Hooper; the other was more interested in her mother, and clung tightly to her black skirt.

'Now what's on your mind, Mrs May?' Hooper demanded. 'Do you know anything about it?'

'Of course I don't,' she answered, and there was a sudden flash of anger in her eyes. 'But I know you police would soon start asking George if *he* knew anything.'

'Where was your brother last night?'

So this was the widow who worked at the Hall and ran the gardeners' cottage home.

'He was home, abed, where a good man ought to be,' she answered.

'From eight o'clock?' Scepticism was loud in Hooper's voice. Roger switched off his engine, and Snell leaned forward, as if fascinated by what must be one of the oddest interrogations they had heard. Hooper's roughness was only partly real; there was a kind of kindliness in the way he looked at the children, both of whom were now staring at him. They looked plump, clean, warm, well. 'Now come on, Mrs May, where was George last night?'

'He was indoors, I tell 'ee.'

'And what about your father?'

'He was abed, he always goes to bed after supper, he lies in listening to the wireless and reading his newspaper. Don't you go saying it was my brother George or Dad, they didn't know anything about it, that's a fact.'

'You won't help George or anyone else by lying,' Hooper said. 'Was he in all last night?'

'Yes, I tell 'ee, 'ee was!'

Hooper said: 'I hope you're right. Better hop in the back, I'm going to see him.' He leaned out and opened the rear door and the children suddenly became excited at the prospect of a ride. George Ansell's sister got in, hesitantly. Hooper hardly waited for her to sit down before slamming the door. Then he twisted round, gave Roger a broad wink, and drove on. The whole incident had taken no more than sixty seconds, but it was another indication of how well Hooper knew the people around here; and it showed how much tension there was in Mrs May.

She would know all about the bitter enmity between her family and the Cartwrights.

People were gathered near the house, the doors of which were closed; the windows were closed too, and despite the gloom no lights showed inside. Two cars, one of them a hackney carriage and the other a small sports car, were drawn up, and there were two men standing by each. Roger recognized the camera of newspapermen; the flash of light as he drew up didn't surprise him.

'What have you got for us, Handsome?' one of the men called out.

'See you at the station, about seven,' Roger answered.

'Have a heart. That right you've found young Cartwright's body?'

'Later,' said Roger.

Hooper had driven on. Outside the kitchen garden there was an ambulance, more cars including a doctor's, and at least five newspapermen, with cameras. Questions were flung at Roger and Hooper as they got out, and one man tried to pull Snell aside.

'If you want a broken nose, do that again,' Snell said.

The newspaperman grinned and let them pass.

Inside the kitchen garden there was a ring of policemen and the patch being prepared for the spring and early summer vegetables was cordoned off. The tools remained there, just as they had been when the men had stopped working. The pathetically small body was on a stretcher, covered with a sheet. The official police photographers had finished with that, and were now taking close-ups of the vegetable trench, and others were pouring plaster of Paris into footprints in the loose soil. By the far wall, guarded by two uniformed policemen, were the Ansells. Near them was Colonel Madden, standing almost forlornly.

Madden had the look of an army man run to seed; that showed in his coarse skin, veined and slightly bulbous nose, and loose mouth. But he had a stamp of quality about him, too; dressed in breeches and gaiters, an old Norfolk jacket and a green pork-pie hat, he was obviously 'gentry'.

And his sister had thrown him out of the Hall because of his *affaires*.

A man came hurrying from the main group to meet Hooper, and he glanced at West almost hopefully.

'You help to dig him out?' Roger asked.

'Yes, sir.'

'Been identified?'

'Did that myself, sir – there's an injury to the face, sir.'

'How'd he die, d'you think?'

'Knife wound in the carotid artery, rather a lot of bleeding, I would say. That's as far as I know, sir, it's what it looked like.' The man was making sure that he was not suspected of knowing what the pathologist would say.

What he said certainly explained the bloodstains in the old Austin.

'Talked to anyone?' asked Roger, while Hooper glanced about him. He was staring at the older Ansell, who stood some distance off, with a plainclothes man by his side. Old Jake looked as craggy as a rock, the lines etched deep on his face, the grey stubble spikey and harsh. His son, less craggy, was also less poised. He kept putting a cigarette to his lips, drawing at it, and then holding it down by his side, as if he were afraid of being seen with it alight. His sister and two children went to him, and he glanced down at them, and then at Hooper: obviously Hooper worried him far more than Roger did.

'We want some place where we can question the Ansells,' Roger said quietly. 'And we want this crowd moved.'

'Not so easy,' Hooper growled. 'They're the searchers we laid on, can't blame them for wanting to find out all they can now the body's turned up.' He drew a deep breath, and then turned to a plainclothes man standing near. 'Frobisher, get the people away. Tell the Press there'll be a statement tonight.' He turned again, to Colonel Madden, who had drawn near, and for once seemed nonplussed. 'We'd like to talk to the Ansells indoors somewhere.'

'You can take them to their cottage . . .' Madden began.

'Too far away.' Hooper was brusque. 'May we use yours, Colonel?'

Madden didn't fancy that, and gnawed at his moustache, before conceding:

'Suppose so. Yes, all right.' He had a deep voice; Snell would call it 'fruity'.

'Thank you, sir,' Hooper said, almost perfunctorily. 'This way, Mr West.'

Madden went off, as if reluctantly.

'Tell you what,' Roger whispered to Hooper, as the detective named Frobisher began to try to move the crowd. 'Ask if anyone here saw anyone come into the kitchen garden up to half past three, when the body was found. Make them feel like as if we've taken them into our confidence.'

'Good idea,' said Hooper, and raised his voice; he could be stentorian whenever he wanted. 'Listen to me, everybody! We want to know of anyone who came into the kitchen garden apart from the Ansells – we'd expect them to be here. If any of you were around and saw someone else, tell one of my men, or report to the police station at Arncott, or Police Constable Bicker at Foley. All clear?'

Two or three of the crowd called 'yes'. There was a general brightening in their expressions, and Hooper managed a quick grin.

'You ought to be a public-relations man,' he said. 'Anything special you want done here?'

'Your chaps don't need teaching their ABC,' Roger said, to put the local man into an amiable mood. 'Which way is Madden's cottage?'

'That gate, and to the right.' Hooper led the way, and

plainclothes men came with the Ansells, who had not uttered a word. Widowed Mrs May did not come with them, but watched with her children; there was no doubt that she was badly frightened. Roger caught a glimpse of her as she looked at Syd Cartwright's shrouded body.

There was a lawn at the back of the great house, and flower beds, with wallflowers looking bushy and healthy. The kitchen garden was hidden from the lawn by its high red-brick wall, and by several tall oak trees, which seemed to carve forbidding patches out of the darkening sky. The whole countryside had a bleaker look than it had an hour ago.

Among the trees was a small, brick-built cottage, and lights were on in two rooms. To reach it, they had to pass the domestic quarters of the Hall.

The cottage had a big front room, furnished in the worst Victorian fashion, with plush-covered chairs and sofas, photographs on the walls, a threadbare carpet which had once been very good. The flowered wallpaper was peeling near the ceiling. Everything had an air of decayed gentility, and a 17-inch television set had an incongruous look.

'Close the front door and make sure no one gets too near, Frobisher,' Hooper said to a man. 'Hill, you can go back and make sure there's no trouble with that crowd about.'

'Right, sir.'

Roger and Hooper went into the big room, and the door closed, leaving the two Ansells together with the two detectives. The old man, who had walked as if half crippled with rheumatism, stood upright as a post, staring at the window overlooking the sweeping lawn and the oaks, and the Hall beyond. His son could not keep still, and his eyes were glittering. The old man's eyes were very deepset; like pools of stagnant water.

Hooper said: 'This is Superintendent West of Scotland Yard. Just answer his questions.'

The old man didn't move; George glanced at Roger, and asked in a grating voice:

'What did you bring us in here for? Might as well tell everyone you think we killed the Cartwrights.'

Roger asked mildly: 'Didn't you?'

George raised clenched fists.

'We didn't even see them, haven't set eyes on them for weeks. We didn't kill no one.'

'Have you been with your father every minute of the time since eight o'clock last night?'

George hesitated, and looked puzzled and wary.

'Supposing I haven't?'

'If you have you can speak for both of you. If he's been alone part of the time, you can speak for yourself.'

George muttered: 'Damn trickery.'

'Now listen,' said Roger, 'we just want to get at the facts. We've got to ask you some questions which would be damaging if the newspapermen were to hear – probably worse if your neighbours were to hear. If you didn't have anything to do with the murders, you've nothing to fear, but if you behave as if you're frightened out of your wits, don't be surprised if people jump to conclusions. Now – ready?'

'Yes.' George looked startled.

'Forget last night, and concentrate on this morning. Have you been out in Lady Foley's car?'

'No.'

'Has your father?'

The old man startled Roger by speaking in a low-pitched, deliberate voice; and he made them all swing towards him.

'I can answer for myself,' he said. 'I don't depend on no man to speak for me.'

'Good. Have you been out in her ladyship's car today?'

'No, nor in fifty days.'

'Have you been in the kitchen garden all day?'

'Most on't, there or in the greenhouses,' George said, and his father nodded.

'At what times have you been in the greenhouses?' asked Roger.

' 'Bout an hour, from twelve to one, and again 'bout twenty minutes, when Colonel Madden called us to the house about the search.'

'Was the garden empty at any other time?'

'No,' answered George flatly.

'When did you start digging the patch where the body was found?'

'S'morning.'

'Wasn't it started last night?'

'No, it weren't.'

Roger said: 'Well, you know what this means, don't you? Either you buried that body, or someone sneaked in and buried it when you were out. Positive the garden wasn't left empty before twelve o'clock?'

'Yes.'

'Don't you have a morning tea-break?'

'There's a thermos of tea we bring with us.' George moistened his lips. 'I tell you no one come in while we were there, and we didn't—'

His father began to speak again, talking his son down, as he had probably done most of his life. It was fascinating to see the way his lips moved; his chin actually worked all the time that he spoke, like that of a ventriloquist's doll.

'Speak for yourself, George Ansell,' he said again. 'I was out of the garden twice, once to talk to her ladyship, once to go and see if there were any rats in the trap by the stables. I weren't in the garden all the time.'

His son stared at him, eyes suddenly touched with horror, but the old man's lips closed like a trap. He had said his piece and he had made it clear that George – his own son – had had an opportunity to bury the body unseen.

Hooper broke his long silence.

'Did you see anyone else go into the garden, Jake?'

'No.'

Hooper looked at George.

'Did you?'

Very slowly, George shook his head.

'You'd better be sure about this,' Hooper went on, 'because if no one else went into that garden, and if that patch was freshly dug this morning—'

'I didn't do it!' cried George, and his eyes were blazing. 'I didn't have it in for the Cartwrights, either, but he's hated them for years!'

Now George glared at his father, who showed no sign at all that he had heard.

The moment of silence was broken outside the room, not inside. First there were sharp footsteps, then a man's voice, and then Lady Foley's, sharp and clear.

'Nonsense. Open the door.'

Almost at once the door opened.

CHAPTER XII

FACTS?

LADY FOLEY came in with a kind of restrained violence; as if she was bottling up her anger, but Roger believed that much that she did was for effect. Hooper frowned, but obviously wished she hadn't come; there was no way of preventing the local man from feeling awkward in the presence of one of the 'county'. Doubtless Hooper saw the closed ranks of the county aligned behind Lady Foley, and was especially anxious not to put a foot wrong.

She glanced at the Ansells, ignored Hooper, and said to Roger:

'Have you made any charge?'

'No, my lady, we're just getting at facts.'

'Is it your custom to get at facts by making the whole neighbourhood think that innocent people are under arrest?'

'We can't help it if people jump to conclusions,' Roger said.

'You could act with more consideration and discretion. My gardeners know nothing about the murders or the death of the horse. Nor do I.'

Roger said sharply: 'What's your purpose? Do you want to stop this interrogation? Are you afraid of what these men might say?'

Hooper's eyes applauded.

'I won't have them browbeaten.'

'I won't have interference in the course of an investigation,' Roger said. 'But as you're here, answer some questions, please.'

Hooper's eyes were glowing, the Ansells looked aghast, and Lady Foley stood silent.

'Did you go to Mr Gale's stables last night?' Roger demanded.

'I was indoors all last night. I told you so earlier.'

'People forget a lot when they're in danger,' Roger said. 'Did you hire anyone to go and kill Shoestring?'

'That is an impertinent—'

'Did you hire anyone to go and kill that horse? Did you persuade these two men to go and do your foul work for you?' Roger pointed a finger at the Ansells, and had the satisfaction of seeing Jake gape, and George look astounded. Lady Foley was taken completely aback, but quickly recovered and said: 'I am quite capable of carrying out my own dirty work, as you call it. Now if—'

'Did you give anyone permission to use your car this morning?' Roger flashed.

'No.'

'Last night?'

Lady Foley said: 'George—' and broke off, seeing the expression in young Ansell's eyes. 'What difference does it make?'

'It could make a lot. Did George have permission to use your car last night?'

She hesitated.

George Ansell said hopelessly: 'Yes, I did. Her ladyship was kind enough to let me use it. I wanted – I wanted to see some friends in Reading.'

'So you drove past Arncott Stables last night?'

'Yes.'

'At what time?'

'It – it would be about eight o'clock, going, and about half past ten coming back.' George answered reluctantly. 'You don't have to tell me more. I was there about the time the horse and old Cartwright were killed, and I could have killed his son and buried him. But – but I didn't, that's God's truth. I didn't do it, m'lady.'

'I think you'd better come along to the station with us,' Roger said briskly. George looked helplessly at his mistress, and there was compassion in her eyes; he did not even glance at his father; the father who had refused the son an alibi he could easily have made.

*   *   *

'I do not believe that George Ansell committed these crimes,' Lady Foley said. 'I know of no reason why he should.'

'Do you know of any reason why his father is so hostile?'

'Yes.' She was quite matter-of-fact. 'George is having an *affaire* with the wife of one of John Gale's stable-hands. That is why he takes the car into Reading. Old Jake had bitter memories of a similar kind of *affaire*, and won't lift a hand to help his son because of it. George was with the woman last night, of course, but daren't say so. It might wreck the woman's marriage, and would cause a big scandal in the village. I don't think he will make any confession, Superintendent, but you are quite wrong if you think that he committed the crime. I know George Ansell only too well.'

'Who is the woman?' asked Roger.

'I really think there are some things you should find out for yourselves,' she said tartly.

Roger said, with deceptive mildness: 'We find it all out eventually, Lady Foley. Motives, causes, effects, everything. Good afternoon.'

Hooper had already taken George Ansell into Arncott, and apparently the crowd had followed either them or the ambulance. It was now a clear, starlit night. No one was about. Roger did not see Colonel Madden, and wondered if he could account for his movements last night. He was quite sure that Madden had not been the rider he had seen near the burning car; he was too fat and heavy looking. It could have been Lady Foley; might well have been a woman, in a riding kit. He remembered that Kathleen Russell had been stranded up here with a lame horse; she might have been near the wrecked car, too. There was no way of being sure whether she had any reason for wanting to help Lionel Foley. He could not rid his mind of the possibility that Kathleen Russell knew Foley better than anyone had yet suggested. As he drove down the winding private road, he made some mental notes. The great tower made a black shape against the stars; he wondered if it would be worth stationing a man on top there, by day if not by night; anyone there could see all the callers at the Hall.

Only a police guard was on duty at the Night Shed. The yard was quiet, the work on the horses having been finished for the night. The smell of the stables seemed very oppressive, and there was a slight mist everywhere; the air seemed warmer than it had at midday.

Roger went into the shed and jotted down some notes.

Check Lionel F – Kathleen Russell.　　? Previous acquaintance.

Check Lionel Foley's London associates and Countryman's Club – call the Yard.

Check Silver Monarch's owner – Gerald Corrison.

Check reason Daphne G's dislike Lady F.

Check Colonel Madden; is he so hard up that he had to turn in that story to the racing journals?

Check identity of woman with whom George A is having an *affaire*.

Check insurance on Silver Monarch, and who would benefit.

Check times that Lady Foley's Austin seen on the road and on the drive.

If body deliberately planted in the kitchen garden was this to involve the gardeners – or the Foleys – or simply because it had to be done quickly?

Check identity anyone seen driving the Austin today.

Re-check Lionel F's reasons for wanting to destroy it.

Roger ran through all these, tucked the pad into his pocket, then looked up as he heard the footsteps of a man approaching. The yard was well lit, and he saw everything clearly. A stable lad was carrying two buckets of water to one of the boxes, and two others, obviously spruced up, were going towards the gates, which were closed, with the policeman standing by the side of the wicket gate.

Then John Gale appeared.

'Hallo, Mr Gale.' Roger stood up.

'I thought I saw you come in,' Gale said. 'I wondered if you would care to come in for a drink.'

'Nice of you,' Roger said. There was time; and he could have a word with the Gales and perhaps find out more that he didn't yet know. There might be an ulterior motive in Gale's invitation, too. 'I'd like to, thanks. I'll have a word with Hooper on the phone, and check that I'm not wanted.'

Gale said: 'Right. Is it true you've charged George Ansell?'

'He's being questioned, that's all.' Roger lifted the telephone and dialled the police station number. 'Put me on to Mr Hooper, please.' He watched Gale, noting how good-looking the man was, realizing that he could not be more than thirty-four or -five. He and his wife seemed perfectly matched.

Hooper came on the line. 'That you, West?'

'Yes. Anything urgent in for me?'

'Don't think so, but my missis wants you to come round for dinner,' Hooper said. 'I must have sold her on you being a human being. George A's made a statement, but it doesn't vary from what it was at the house. I can't find the woman he's supposed to be thick with, that could be just to fob us off, not often there's a juicy bit of scandal like that our chaps don't know. The Yard hasn't got anything definite on young Foley – he was at his club all right, but there are a lot of time gaps. Your pals are still checking. His ankle isn't broken, but he can only hobble about – he's on his way home now. Haven't found a single witness to say that any stranger was seen in the Austin, or in that kitchen garden. It all looks as if it points to George Ansell.'

'Make sense to you?'

'Don't know it all, yet,' Hooper responded, 'and I wouldn't

like to commit myself to an opinion on the telephone, anyhow. No one ever tell you that telephones have ears?'

Roger grinned.

'I was told once,' he said. 'What time's dinner?'

'Supper, really. Suit yourself, we usually eat about half past seven.'

'I'll be at the station at seven-fifteen, and you can take me round,' said Roger. 'Thank your wife, won't you?'

'Eat first, give thanks afterwards,' Hopper said, and it was easy to imagine his grin now that he had recovered from the shock and the disappointment at knowing that there had been a second murder.

Roger rung off.

Gale said: 'I've never had much to do with your chaps, but you take it all pretty calmly, don't you?'

'Wouldn't help much if we got steamed up.'

'No. It's difficult for us to be quite so detached,' said Gale, and there was a curious expression in his dark eyes. 'I've known Ted Cartwright for years, and I've always had a soft spot for his son. I can hardly think about what's happened without wanting to go and break someone's neck.'

Roger said: 'I know the feeling.' He went out, and nodded to the constable who was on guard. He wondered where Snell was, and felt sure that he was burrowing deeply, hoping that he would come upon some mine of information. 'You've two reasons for hating the killer, haven't you?'

'Sentiment and hard logic,' Gale answered, and shrugged. 'Yes. It will take me a long time to recover from this, even if I ever get over it. I would say that it will cost me at least a thousand pounds a year for the next year or two – two owners have already changed their minds about coming to me, and at least two will move. I can't say I blame them; I wasn't doing too well for them anyhow.'

'Satisfied that Silver Monarch was killed in mistake for Shoestring?'

Gale said quietly: 'No. Are you?'

'I'm not satisfied about anything, yet,' Roger answered. 'What other motives would you suggest?'

'A possible one was to kill the Monarch,' Gale said.

'How heavily was the horse insured?'

'Twenty thousand pounds,' Gale answered, 'but Corrison, the owner, had plenty of money, that wasn't the reason. Corrison used to live near here, took his horses away when Lord Foley was having his string trained at Arncott, and came back a year or two ago.'

'Why'd he move away?' asked Roger.

'Corrison and old Foley didn't get on too well,' Gale answered, 'and Colonel Madden disliked him, too. That's old meat, though. The horse was going to carry a fortune on the Derby, and you can take it from me that no other horse really had a chance,' Gale went on. 'I know there's many a slip, but everything being equal, I think Monarch would have walked away with the Classics. There was always a danger of it being got at.'

'Doped?'

'Or injured.' Gale gave a short laugh, and there was an ugly note in it. 'You don't need soft soap, West. I love this whole business – the training, the horses themselves, the excitement of the racing, and the betting – it's something which you can never get out of your system once it's in. But there's an ugly side. A lot of people stand to win big money now that the field for the Classics is open. Don't let anyone tell you differently. For what it's worth, I think the story of Lady Foley's threat to kill Shoestring gave someone a heaven-sent chance, and they took it. I wish to God I hadn't had a night watch. Better to be ruined completely than to feel both Cartwrights were killed because they were trying to do my job for me.'

A voice came out of the dusk.

'For heaven's sake, John, don't talk like that.' It was Gale's wife. 'It's bad enough to have to face what's happened, without you trying to persuade yourself that you were responsible. Can't you make him understand that he wasn't, Mr West?'

She came from the gate leading into the garden; and in this dim light, she looked so beautiful that she wasn't quite real. Roger had not realized how small she was before; he had only seen her on the London stage, and not thought of her as a person.

'Look, Daff, we both know how I feel, let's not argue about it,' Gale pleaded.

'I'll try not to,' said Daphne. 'I'm very glad you were able to come, Superintendent. One of your suspects is here, too – at least he says he's a suspect.'

'Who?'

'Lionel Foley,' Daphne answered. 'That's why I came out the back way. He called to see Kath, and I thought you might not want to see him socially.'

There was the Kathleen Russell–Lionel Foley association in the air again.

Roger grinned.

'The boot's on the other foot! Is he able to walk?'

'With a stick, yes. He came from the hospital by taxi. Mr West, is it true he tried to destroy his mother's car?'

'He drove off at a hell of a bat, anyway,' Roger said.

He surprised both the Gales into a laugh.

'Did he set fire to it?'

'No – someone else did.'

'Did you know——' began Daphne, only to be cut short when her husband said sharply:

'Daff, don't start spreading rumours.'

'This isn't a rumour, pet, this I saw with my own eyes,' his wife said, cooing; but there was underlying tartness in her voice. 'Mr West, my husband is doing his best to appear in the role of a fine stiff-lipped, stiff-necked English gentleman, but I haven't the same high standards.'

'Daff, stop it!'

'I will not,' she retorted, and took Roger's arm. 'I happened to know that Lady Foley, *dear* Lady Foley, has always hated us being here. When we bought the stables she thought we would fail in a year or two, and she's bitterly disappointed because we began to make a success of it. If she had her way, the stables would go derelict, and the whole place would fall down and rot away. That's how much she hates everything to do with horses and horse-racing.'

'She rides,' Roger pointed out.

'Oh, she doesn't mind a little hunting,' Daphne conceded. 'That's true to type, too, she probably squeals with delight when she sees the fox being torn to pieces by the hounds. You will gather that I do not like blood sports.'

They were very near the front door.

'Cut it out,' Gale persisted, but obviously he had little hope that she would.

Daphne pressed Roger's arm.

'I'll come to the point quickly,' she said. 'Lady Foley may seem a normal human being, but she is so full of hate and suppressed desire for revenge that she isn't normal. How *can* she be? She lives with the wreckage of her life all about her. When she married, her husband owned Foley Hall, the Park, and half of the land around here. She watched him gamble it all away. I don't say she isn't to be pitied, but imagine what that could do to a mind. I've thought for years that she was unbalanced, and having a brother who spends half his money on the bottle and scratches a living supplying gossip pars to racing newspapers hasn't exactly helped. When her dearly beloved son started in the family tradition, I think something snapped. And I think she sent George Ansell down to kill *both* Silver Monarch and Shoestring. George would do whatever she told him, he hates everything to do with racehorses, being an Ansell; that was drilled into him. And if he was surprised in Silver Monarch's box, and saw Ted Cartwright, the man who ruined his mother, well, *is* it surprising that he would hit him hard enough to kill him? And is it surprising that Lady Foley will protect him in every way she can?'

There was a long silence when Daphne stopped. They were on the porch of the house, and a light was on behind the curtains in a front room, but there was no sound until a car swished by; then a Vespa motor-cycle went pop-pop-pop-pop along.

'Two birds with one stone, eh?' Roger said, in a matter-of-fact voice.

Daphne laughed.

'You see, darling, he doesn't think I'm being bitchy. Exactly, Mr West – two birds with one stone; in fact, three. Stopping her son from wasting his future; getting her own back on John, for keeping the stables alive in Foley; and getting her own back on horses generally. She was near the car when it was being burnt, this afternoon. I saw a single rider moving off, and I happened to have my field glasses with me. She was riding away from that burning car – I'm *quite* certain.'

* * *

Why should Daphne Gale make such a dead set on Lady Foley? Roger asked himself as he waited for a call to the Yard to come through. Hardy was still in his office. He promised to check all Lionel Foley's London associates, and to check on Kathleen Russell, as well as to find out if Daphne Gale had any past associations with the Foleys; any cause for hate. And he was able to confirm that Corrison, the owner of Silver Monarch and who was then in the United States, was a wealthy man.

'Someone else could have insured the horse, mind you,' Hardy said. 'We'll keep at it. There's one thing.'

'Yes.'

'Young Foley wasn't actually seen after six o'clock that night, although next morning he was in bed at the club just after seven. We're still checking his movements.'

'Thanks.'

'Don't let anyone else get killed, will you?' Hardy said bluffly.

'I didn't plan to,' Roger said. 'Anyone in mind?'

'Any other witness, especially if the boy was killed to make sure he couldn't identify the killer. You know that as well as I do.'

'Yes,' agreed Roger, and rang off.

He knew the danger; it was one he had to live with. You couldn't protect anyone you didn't know.

CHAPTER XIII

LADY FRIEND

'MY GOD,' gasped Hooper. 'If her ladyship set that car on fire, and we can prove it, we've got her.'

'If you talk shop and let that pudding get cold, I'll get you,' threatened his wife.

'Nothing's going to make me let it get cold, it smells too good,' Roger said. 'I'm sorry I let that out then.' He took a laden plate which Hooper's wife handed to him, and helped himself to potatoes and peas. It was an enormous steak pudding, and the crust looked as if it would melt in his mouth.

Hooper shovelled potatoes on to his plate.

Mrs Hooper was a massive woman, nearly as tall as her husband; if she didn't dwarf Hooper, at least she was a match for him. She was wearing a navy-blue dress with a square neck, and it was a little too tight for her enormous bosom. Her cheeks were flushed from the heat of the kitchen, her blue eyes had a twinkle, and she put more potatoes on her plate than Hooper had on his.

'Think Mrs Gale'd say this in court?' Hooper demanded.

'If we want her to,' Roger said.

'Shurrup,' ordered Mrs Hooper.

Hooper paused in eating to take a great gulp of beer, and put down a silver tankard with a bang which made the table silver rattle.

'It's all right, he knows you can cook by now,' he said. 'If you ask me, Mrs Gale's got her head screwed on the right way. It all adds up.'

'It adds up almost too neatly.'

'Don't you *want* to finish this job quick? If it was me, I'd be so anxious to get back to the bosom of my family that I'd have had Lady F. on a charge by now.'

'Perhaps your family wouldn't want you back,' remarked Mrs Hooper. 'More gravy, Mr West?' Suddenly she looked startled at his nearly empty plate. 'I mean, more *pie*. I thought Bert could—'

'Put it away, I know,' said Roger. 'He didn't warn you that I only had a sandwich for lunch. Thanks very much ... it's wonderful.' He saw that Hooper was taken aback, too; he had made little inroad into his meal. For the next three minutes they concentrated on eating, and then Hooper asked: 'Well, wouldn't a charge shake her?'

'It might. She was shaken when we brought George away.'

'That's another thing,' Hooper said. 'We can't keep George Ansell all night unless we charge him. Think we've enough for a charge? The Old Man will give the okay if you say so. Add it up: down here last night at the right time, won't say who he was with, no alibi, this woman friend doesn't exist as far as we can tell. He can drive that Austin. He was alone in the garden for long enough to bury that body.'

'We'll go into details *after* dinner, please,' said Mrs Hooper.

'Lucy, put a sock in it,' said Hooper. 'Never known you have such sensitive feelings before. And George could have driven that car down and picked young Cartwright up. He was alone long enough. He could use the car more or less when he wanted to – don't take any notice of this permission nonsense. The car's always in the yard behind the kitchen garden, and there's a road leading to the private road through the Hall park. He had opportunity for both crimes, don't make any mistake about that.'

'We've evidence that a woman was driving,' Roger reminded him.

'Her nibs is in it with him, that's the size of it,' declared Hooper. 'Don't get me wrong, Handsome, I don't think murder was ever intended, but once it was done they were in it, sink or swim.'

'There's plenty left,' Mrs Hooper announced.

'Er—' began Roger.

'Oh, come on, I like to leave an empty dish, and you don't know what a joy it is to see someone really enjoy his food.'

'You'd have to be a fool not to enjoy this. Bert doesn't deserve it, does he?'

'Been telling him that for years,' Mrs Hooper said.

'The thing is,' Roger said to Hooper a few minutes later, 'Supposing you're wrong? Supposing you find this woman whom George Ansell is having an *affaire* with.'

'I tell you she doesn't exist,' insisted Hooper.

His wife looked at him straightly, said, 'Cocky tonight, Bert, aren't you?' and got up to clear the table, handing the dirty crockery and cutlery through a hatch to a woman on duty for the evening. Hooper watched his wife, as if he realized there was deep significance in her last remark. He waited until she had brought a huge trifle, spread thick with whipped cream, and a deep dish apple pie, as well as a jug of cream whipped so that a spoon stood up with it; then he said:

'Let's have it, Lucy. What do you know?'

'One at a time, Mr West, or both together?' inquired Lucy Hooper, with nice consideration.

'May I have the pie first?'

'Certainly – and pass Mr West the cream, Bert,' said Mrs Hooper, obviously savouring her secret to the utmost. She handed Roger a plate of apple pie and Hooper passed the cream and sugar. 'It's about time that you realized that a policeman doesn't necessarily know everything,' went on Mrs Hooper sweetly. 'You may know what goes on under your noses but if you have to look a little further afield – oh, no.'

'What are you getting at?' Hooper was sharp.

She beamed at him.

'All right, duck, I'll put you out of your misery. You may be surprised, but George Ansell has been seen going into the pictures in Reading more than once with —' She broke off. 'Is that all right, Mr West?'

'*Who was he seen with?*' roared Hooper.

'Mabel Cartwright as was, Mabel Tree as she is now, and

Syd's sister,' answered Mrs Hooper. 'Wife of one of Mr Gale's stable lads, you know. And it's no use letting your eyes pop out of your head, I know it's true because I saw them go in myself once. I don't go spreading a lot of gossip, and the trouble between the Ansells and the Cartwrights has been bad enough for twenty years as it is. But you can take it from me that George Ansell was with Mabel Tree née Cartwright last night.' Mrs Hooper gave a surprisingly giggly laugh. 'Tree née Cartwright,' she repeated. 'Hasn't tree née got a funny sound?'

*　　　*　　　*

'If this is true, there'd be a strong motive for a Cartwright killing Ansell,' Roger pointed out sharply. 'Would it work the other way round?'

'If Ted knew about it and was going to make trouble it would be a motive all right,' Hooper agreed.

'I've heard the name Tree before in this job,' Roger commented. 'Wasn't he one of the men who saw the Foley Austin near the stables last night?'

'Good God!' exclaimed Hooper gaspingly. 'Yes. Who are we going to tackle first? George Ansell, Tree, or Mabel Tree?'

'Mabel, I think,' Roger said. 'But we don't want a lot of gossip, and if one of your chaps goes round to question her there'll be plenty. Where does she live?'

'Copse Road, just on the outskirts of Arncott, on the Foley side,' answered Hooper. 'Five minutes' drive. I could drive you to a corner of the street, and—'

'I'll go myself, as soon as I've had coffee – finishing touch to a wonderful meal, Mrs Hooper, thank you very much. Would you like to do something else for me?'

'It would be a pleasure.'

'If your husband doesn't mind hobnobbing with mere Detective Inspectors, ask my Inspector Snell round one evening, while he's still here. It will teach him that good cooks still exist.'

'Why don't you both come?' Mrs Hooper invited, her eyes lighting up. 'I will say you don't mind saying what's on your mind, it's a nice change. Bert, don't stand there looking like a lost soul, ask Mr West what liqueur he'll have. We always bring back a bottle of liqueur from the Continent every year,' she confided in Roger.

Roger sat back in an armchair in a lounge which would have served in a show house anywhere. It was pleasantly warm in front of the coal fire, he had eaten too much, there was coffee in front of him and apricot liqueur in a small glass by the side of the coffee. The glow of well-being was golden. It would make no difference what time he reached Mrs Tree; the difficulty would be to get her husband away so that he could talk to her on her own.

He found himself wondering if Tree's evidence about the Foley Austin was reliable. It had been corroborated, but Hooper would have to make sure that there was no collusion between witnesses.

'I think you'd better send a man round for Tree, and keep him at the station with questions about the Austin last night – and about the Cartwrights at the stable,' Roger said. 'Half an hour will be all I need to talk to his wife.' He sipped first the coffee, then the liqueur. 'What is she like?'

'She's like all the Cartwright women, plump and pretty,' answered Hooper. 'I would never have believed—'

His wife interrupted him.

'You'd have got round to it some time before Christmas,' she said, and Roger found himself chuckling.

He was so sure that there was no hurry.

*　　*　　*

Mabel Tree stared at the evening newspaper which her husband had brought in, about the time that Roger was entering the Hoopers' dining-room. She stood in the small living-room of the house, near the heath, and within sight of the training stables. She was a woman with a beauty-contest figure and a beauty-contest face, but just now she was white-cheeked, and her eyes glittered as if with fear, as well as grief. The report said that Mr George Ansell had been taken to the police station for questioning; and worse, there were pictures of George, standing by the ambulance, and standing by a heap on the ground – over her own brother, a heap covered with a sheet or a blanket. Other people were in the picture, but she saw no one except that covered figure, and she could see the horror on George's face.

She could understand why.

She heard her husband upstairs, whistling shrilly. He would soon be down. She glanced up at the ceiling, and then closed her eyes, as if the burden of grief wondering what Fred would say and do was too great for her. Her fair hair was untidy, she wore a two-piece suit of loosely knitted nylon, her hands were white and shapely, and her legs and ankles trim and neat.

Fred came hurrying down the stairs.

She did not wonder, then, as she had before, whether the affair would have happened had they had children. She was past speculating. She folded the newspaper and put it on his chair, and wondered. Fred was so cold about death. At least he would put her distress down wholly to the death of her father and of Syd. He wouldn't dream that she and George—

Only George, the living, seemed to matter.

Fred stopped halfway down the stairs, and went up again; that was like him, he was always forgetting things. The only things he never forgot were his precious horses. It was even possible that he would stand at the bedroom window and look out, where he could see the lights of Arncott Stables. He had been more upset about Silver Monarch than her father, but the horse had not been one of his charges and he had become much more cheerful when he had realized that he was now grooming one of the best horses in the stable. She heard him moving about – and then heard the front door bell ring.

She stared through the open doorway towards the front door. Then she jolted into movement, and hurried to open it.

It might be anyone. People had been so kind, not dreaming of her great cause for fear: that someone might find out about her and George. Her heart began to thump; it thumped a great deal, these days, and that grew worse when she saw a heavily-built man whose face wasn't very clear in the dim light from the hall.

'Mrs Tree?'

'Yes,' she said. 'Who—'

'I'm a newspaperman, Mrs Tree,' the heavily-built man said. 'I want to talk to you about your association with George Ansell.'

She felt as if he had stabbed her with a knife. She could not speak, could only stand staring at him, while her mind shrieked a warning – that in a moment her husband would be downstairs, would want to know what this man wanted, and – *How could anyone know about her and George?*

'I know you can't talk here,' the man said. 'If you do what I tell you, no one will ever know anything about it, I'm not interested in doing you any harm. When can I see you?'

'I—' Mabel began, and then her throat seemed to close up. She was too terrified to realize that this approach was peculiar: there was only her fear.

'Who is it, Mabel?' her husband called.

'I'll be at the corner of the road in half an hour,' whispered the caller. 'Don't keep me waiting. Find some excuse.' He turned away, and then said in a louder voice: 'Sorry to have troubled you.'

Mabel said in a squeaky voice: 'It's all right.'

Fred Tree came hurrying down the stairs as she closed the door. She turned to look at him, and although the light was so poor, she was afraid that he would see her pallor.

'Someone – someone called at the wrong house,' she said. 'He wanted – wanted Hill Street.'

'Got eyes in his head, hasn't he?' asked Tree. 'Mabel, have you seen that rosette, the red winner one I got two years ago at the Lincoln Show?'

He was always gloating over the rosettes, the prizes he won, the little triumphs he had had.

'I think it's in the usual place,' Mabel answered.

'No, it isn't; if it was I'd have found it.'

'I suppose I'd better look,' Mabel said, and pushed past him; at least she could keep her face from him. He didn't come after her, and she half ran up the stairs, driven by a terror which was greater than she had ever known. What excuse could she make to go out? How could she suddenly explain that she had to go? It would have been easier if she had told him when he had first come in, but now she would have to 'remember' some reason. She began to tremble, and minutes passed before she could bring herself to look through the drawer with all his trophies and souvenirs in. She found the rosette, and clutched it tightly as she turned towards the door. It was so awful, although she had no love for him.

It was *awful*.

There was another ring at the front door.

Her heart began to pound, and she could have screamed. 'No, don't come again, don't come!' Suddenly she realized that if Fred opened the door the stranger might talk to him; she felt positive that it was the same man. She went rushing down the stairs. But she need not have worried, for Fred had not stirred himself, he would leave all the chores to her, even today. She was almost panting when she opened the door — and then she seemed to stop breathing, for a policeman in uniform stood outlined against the doorway.

She fell back a pace.

'Sorry to worry you, Mrs Tree,' the policeman said, 'but is Mr Tree in?'

'He – he – he – yes, he's in.'

'We want his help at the station, we're trying to get a clear picture of everything that happened all day yesterday at the stables,' the constable said. 'We won't keep him long – I've a car outside. Do you think it will be too much of a nuisance?'

'Oh, I – I'll tell him,' Mabel said, and then became aware of her husband standing in the doorway of the kitchen; she heard him call:

'Don't tell me someone else needs glasses.'

'It's—' Mabel began.

'It's Constable Wolf here,' the policeman called, and bore patiently with Fred's acid comments about being disturbed in the privacy of his own home. It was five or six minutes before Tree was ready to leave. Mabel had ten minutes, no more, to put on her hat and coat and hurry along to the corner. Thank God she'd got such a chance, it was almost as if fate was on her side. She hurried upstairs for her hat, and was down again ready for the street within two minutes. She would be at the meeting place with five minutes to spare.

She left the lights on, told herself that she must be back in twenty minutes, and no one need ever know she had gone out. She closed the door, without making a sound, glanced up and down, and then went towards the corner. She saw a man turning into the road on the other side, but he appeared to take no notice of her. When she reached the corner, no one was there, but a car was parked nearby, its side lights on.

She waited, shivering, partly through cold, partly through fear.

CHAPTER XIV

THIRD VICTIM?

THE ROW of small houses close to the heath, on the out-skirts of Arncott, had only one street lamp, and that was not burning when Roger turned the corner. He came from an-other, longer road where a few lamps burned, and the gloom of this street was broken by the yellow squares of light at some of the windows. As he turned the corner, he saw a car drawn up, without parking lights, not far away. Any policeman on duty would be after the motorist, for a car swinging round the corner might come upon this obstruction without a chance to avoid it.

Why were some motorists fools?

A door opened, lights shone into the street, and the shadow of a man or woman was thrown into the narrow roadway. Roger had no reason to believe that it was at Number 15, the house he was heading for. The door closed quickly, and next moment a woman's footsteps sounded sharply; hurrying.

There was no reason to think that the woman might be Tree's wife.

The woman crossed the road, still hurrying.

Roger shone his torch on to the front door of a house nearby, and saw the number, 9. Had she come from 15 or 17? He reached Number 17, saw a light shining at the small fan-light, and could see a glow of light through a window, as if the door of that room had been left open. So someone was at home.

There was a small garden, and an open gate; he marvelled that there should be so little ground for these houses when they were so close to the heath, but he was not thinking about that when he rang the bell. He wondered if Syd Cartwright's sister expected the visit; if she had heard what had happened to

George Ansell she would be pretty worked up by that, as well as in great distress about her bereavements. It might be callous, but it was good to feel that she would be in just the mood to talk freely. The key to her confidences would be an assurance that he would not tell the newspapers that she had been with George, unless she was needed for evidence on George's defence. That wouldn't be his, Roger's, responsibility.

No one answered.

He rang the bell again.

Then he heard the engine of a car start up, not far away, and immediately thought of the car without parking lights. Next moment, he heard what sounded like a cry. If it was one, it was quickly stifled. He spun round, towards the corner. The car had been facing this way; if it moved, he would soon see it. The cry seemed to linger on the air, and quite suddenly he ran out of the gateway and raced towards the end of the road. He was close to it when the engine roared, and he saw the dark shape of the car, still without lights. But the one street lamp shone on it, he could see moving figures, and thought that someone was struggling inside the car.

He bellowed: 'Stop there!'

The car roared past, making more noise than speed. He reached the corner. His own car was parked a hundred yards along; he had welcomed the walk, and had not wanted the car to be recognized. He cursed his caution as he ran along the roadway, still seeing the car ahead, a black shape against the greying sky, and thrown up in silhouette against the parking lights of his own car.

The other car swung to the right, towards the main road and the centre of Arncott; and away from the heath. As it went, he saw its lights go on, and the rear light looked very bright, but he was too far away to read the number.

He reached his own car. Some way off, he saw a single wobbling light; the car passed it. He jumped into his seat, and lost a precious second fumbling in the darkness for the keyhole of the ignition; he switched on at last and the engine ticked over promptly. He started racing in the wake of the other car, still able to see its red light, and to see the pale, wobbling light drawing nearer him. As he drew near this he saw that it was a cyclist. He slowed down, and opened his window. Luck was with him, for this man was a uniformed policeman.

He shouted: 'Constable! This is West of the Yard!'

A startled: 'Yes, sir?' came.

'Hurry to a telephone, have a call put out for a Riley Pathfinder, nineteen fifty-five model, the car that passed you just now. Try to get it stopped.'

'Riley Pathfinder, sir, fifty-five?' The man spoke slowly as he was on the turn, looking behind him to the distant red light. Roger rammed the car into second gear, to start off again. 'Just a minute, sir!' He was going to ask for identification, and would lose every chance there was to help. The engine roared and Roger eased out the clutch. '*Just a minute, sir!*' That came with a note of real urgency. 'Go down the Cut – that's right, sir, the Cut! He'll be heading for the main road now. You turn left at the bottom here and then take second right, you'll get to the main road ahead of him, no doubt about that.'

Praise all country coppers!

'Thanks!'

'... I'll get that call in, sir,' Roger heard, as he bellowed his thanks.

First left – no, left at the bottom. Roger switched on his headlamps, and saw a plain wall in front of him, surrounding a private house. He swung left. The road was very narrow, and he almost scraped a wing. Second right, now. He watched the hedges silvered by his headlights, and they cut off the rear light of the other car; how he wanted a glimpse of that bright red glow. Second right, but how far along? He seemed to be riding into pitch darkness of the heath. He knew a little of the topography of the district, enough to know that he was now heading towards Foley Village, and if this road led straight on, it would go north of the Arncott Stables and north of the village.

It would also pass north of Foley Hall.

A pale finger signpost loomed up, becoming vaguely white, as a ghost. Roger jammed on his brakes for the corner, and swung round. A boy and girl stood as if petrified at the side of the road he was entering. The girl's mouth was wide open, her eyes looked glazed with terror. The boy flung himself in front of her. Roger wrenched the wheel, missed them by inches, and slowed down, sweating, furiously angry with himself. He should never have taken that risk; a few inches nearer and he would have mown them both down.

The road was narrow but straight, and now he could see the full beam of the headlamp. He had to force himself to go fast again, but soon the speedometer was hovering on the seventy. A hare leapt out of the hedge on the right, and seemed to be hypnotized. 'Get away,' breathed Roger, and saw its haunches surge as it fled into the hedge. Then he saw the glow of a car's headlamps in the sky, not far away, and realized that this was the main road, the road which led past the private road entrance to Foley House. Was the car the Pathfinder? If it was, it would reach the end of this turning only fifty yards ahead of him. He kept the headlights full on. The other car was moving at great speed, carving the darkness with its light. He saw it pass. It was shiny black, but he could not be positive of the make, it went so fast. He nosed out of the lane, and then rasped into low gear and started after the other car. It had a hundred yards start, not fifty, and was gaining. His speedometer needle seemed to crawl, but soon he was touching the eighty mark. He saw the buildings of the Stables loom up, and the clock face was illuminated. He also saw two constables standing and staring at both cars as they passed. More lights than usual were on at the stables.

He could not be sure that it was the Pathfinder ahead, could not even be positive that Mabel Tree was in it, anyhow. He might have made a complete fool of himself, might have wasted his time, might even have routed out half the police of the district on a wild goose chase.

He saw the glow of the headlights ahead, turned a bend in the road and saw its rear light, and the shape of Foley's Folly. Then all the lights went out, and there was only blackness ahead.

*　　　*　　　*

As she waited on the corner, her coat hugged tightly about her, cold and fright making her shiver, Mabel Tree noticed the black shape of the car nearby, but did not realize that anyone was in it. She noticed the footsteps of the man who had passed her stop; she wondered if it was one of her neighbours, and if so, whether he had recognized her. She began to look up and down, fearful in case the man who had told her to meet him here delayed too long; she must be back before Fred.

Then she heard a creaking sound, and realized that the door of the car was opening. She watched as a man got out. There was enough light from a street lamp for her to recognize the man who had called on her. Another man climbed out of the car on the other side, and both approached her. She felt an even greater fear; but the dread of her husband finding out where she had been last night, dread of the association with George Ansell becoming generally known, was the greater fear.

The thickset man said: 'Glad you could make it, Mrs Tree. We don't want to cause any trouble.' He paused, as if to let that sink in, and then went on: 'It wouldn't do if the newspapers told the world about you and George Ansell would it?'

'No,' she said, and caught her breath. 'No, you said you wouldn't——'

'We just want you to answer a few questions, that's all,' the man said. 'You needn't worry, provided you tell us the truth. But it must be the truth, see.' He paused again, and the other man moved so that he was just at her side. Now she felt a physical fear, realizing at last that this was not the way the newspaper men were likely to ask questions; there was a kind of silent menace in the taller man, who had not yet spoken. 'Understand me? Just tell us the truth.'

'Yes, I will, but – what do you want to know?'

'Has George been in touch with you today?'

'No!'

'Has anyone asked you about him?'

'No,' she said, and raised her hands in an unwitting attitude of prayer. 'No, why should—'

'I mean, have the *police* asked you any questions?'

'No! No, they've sent—'

The thickset man's hand moved and clutched her wrist; he gripped it tightly and painfully, and she gasped, and tried to free herself.

'Let's have it. They've sent what?'

'They sent for Fred. They said they wanted to ask him a few questions,' Mabel gasped. 'It couldn't be about me and George, Fred doesn't know. He—'

'Did you see George last night?'

'I—'

'*Did you?*'

'Yes,' she gasped. 'Yes, he took me to the pictures in Reading! There was no harm in it, there never has been anything wrong, not really.'

Then both men moved on her, and she realized that they were going to push her into the car. She tried to scream, managed only a sharp cry, and felt one man's hand over her lips, the other's round her waist. She was bundled towards the car, and pushed inside. A blow at the side of her head sent her senses reeling, she could not struggle. She felt herself pushed to one side, and the pressure of a man's body heavy against her. She sat crushed, helpless, gasping for breath and terrified. The tyres grated on the loose gravel of the road, and the car jolted forward; the roar of the engine seemed like that of an aeroplane's. She was flung forward, then backwards; but the man still pressed against her, and she was not badly hurt.

She realized that they thought she was unconscious.

She remembered that Syd had been taken away in a car and murdered.

She screamed: 'Let me out!' and pushed against the man and kicked sideways. She must have hit a tender spot, and for a moment the pressure eased. The car was racing along, but all Mabel could think of was getting out. She touched the door handle and pushed it down; the door opened a fraction. She felt a knife-like edge of cold air. Then she was grabbed round the waist and hauled back; and the door slammed.

'Keep her quiet!' rasped the driver.

'Let me go!' she screamed. 'Let me go!' She tried to kick again, but this time the thickset man gripped her wrist and twisted, so that the pain shot up her arm.

Then she felt something soft pressed against her face; one moment she was able to breathe, the next she felt choked as the air was kept out by the billowy cloth.

They were going to suffocate her.

She tried to get her face away from the shroud-like cloth, tried to kick and struggle again; but the man had her arm twisted so that she could not move. He was pressing her tightly against the side of the car, and the pressure of his hand at her mouth behind the cloth seemed to get harder. It wasn't a choking pressure, just kept all air away. She struggled to draw even a short, single breath, and could not.

She felt her senses swimming, knew she was going to lose consciousness. Awareness of pain and tension faded, but her fear had never been so livid. This was the awful fear of death. Despairingly she gave another kick that caught the man on the ankle, and won a moment's easement. She drew her head back and took in two great gulping breaths of air before the cloth was pressed tightly again, and the pressure at her wrist and arm became excruciating.

She was going to faint.

She was going to die.

She heard the man at the wheel say in a vague, distant sort of way:

'Don't mark her.'

The man holding her did not answer. Her head seemed to be filled with a writhing, whirling mass of dark cloud, which was getting darker. There was a tight band at her breast, so tight that she could not think of anything else. She must breathe, must ease that pressure. She felt herself go limp. Then it seemed as if her head was being lifted off her shoulders, and her whole body was floating.

She must breathe.

The pressure eased. She did not quite lose consciousness but lay back, hardly able to think, hardly able to feel relief. But she was breathing, air was hissing through her lips and to her lungs. Then she realized that she was gulping in great breaths of air, and consciousness was coming back. It was like coming out of gas at the dentist's, exactly the same. Her scalp felt tight, as if someone was pulling it from all directions, and she breathed in a series of gasps, but underlying all these facts was a deep joy.

They hadn't killed her.

She glanced sideways at the shape of the man close to her. He was not pressing so heavily against her, but his right hand was firm about her wrist. If she tried to get away, he would twist and hurt again. She could hear her own breathing, and could just hear his. The driver's head and shoulders were clear against the brightness of the headlamps of the car, which was going fast and very smoothly.

If they weren't going to kill her, what were they going to do?

Who were they?

The driver said, without turning round: 'She okay?'

'Yep.'

'Sure you haven't marked her?'

What did they mean by 'marked'?

'Sure as I can be.'

'If they see any marks on the——'

The man by Mabel's side said: 'Shut up!'

'Aw, what difference does it make. Getting soft?'

'You can forget the marks.'

'Forget nothing,' the driver said, but he did not speak again for several seconds. Mabel stared at his back, and the harsh sound of his voice seemed to echo in her ears. She recognized the sinister note, but did not really understand what was meant by 'marks'. Marks on the what?

Marks on the body!

She gave a convulsive heave and cry, and twisted round. For a moment the pressure at her wrist was agonizing. Then the cloth was pushed into her face, nearly suffocating her again. She had so little strength that she relaxed. Her heart was pounding with dreadful fear.

What were they going to do with her? What else could the driver have meant but 'marks on the body'. Oh, God, what was going to happen to her? Syd, Syd, Syd, was this how it happened to you? There was just the road, the headlights, the silvery streaks of telegraph wires, the dark sky, the hedges, the shapes of trees which showed up as if they were glistening with light, and then dropped away into dark shadows. She had no idea where she was, no idea how long she had been near unconsciousness.

The driver said sharply: 'See that?'

'What?'

'That car.'

'The one on the left?'

'Yeh.'

'What about it?'

'Didn't know there was a road there.'

'So what?'

Mabel felt the tension in the driver, and sensed that he was more worried than the thickset man by her side. They went on for a few seconds, and she saw the headlights of a car coming from the left and moving very fast towards this road; for a moment it almost looked as if the two cars would meet. The driver put on speed, and she felt a new kind of fear: that they would crash. She saw the brilliant glow of the other car's headlamps in the sky, glanced left and saw the actual orbs of light as the car came nearer this road.

The driver said: 'I don't like it. What use was it going as fast as that for?'

'Forget it.'

'Like hell I'll forget it. Fix her.'

Mabel gasped and a word seemed to choke her. '*No!*'

'We haven't reached—'

'I'm going to turn off into those trees near the Folly,' the driver said. 'I'm not going to waste any more time. If the car goes past, okay, we'll get her up to the top and toss her over.'

Mabel screamed:

'*No!*'

She saw a vivid picture of Foley's Folly, knew that if she was thrown from the top she would be smashed to death. Why were they doing this to her? Oh, God, why? She tried to turn and to plead, but the cloth was thrust into her face again, and she could not breathe; and soon she could not move.

The car swung off the road, the lights went out, the engine stopped. She was only vaguely aware of all this, only vaguely aware of the car which was coming up from behind, its headlights blazing. She had no awareness of the tension in this car as the other drew nearer, for the pressure was making her head swim, and terror was paralysing her.

The writhing mists were in her head, the awful pressure was at her breast and at her throat again, she had no strength and she had no hope.

She heard the driver speak, but did not distinguish the note of relief and satisfaction as he said:

'It's gone past.'

Nor did she notice the glow of the following car's headlamps loom very bright, bathe them for a moment behind the trees, and then pass, taking all hope with it.

CHAPTER XV

FOLEY'S FOLLY

ROGER THOUGHT tensely: 'I wish I knew the country-side better,' as he stared at the darkness beyond the beam of his car headlamps. He thought that the other car had swung to the right; if it had, that would be towards Foley Hall, somewhere near the great tower of Foley's Folly. He remembered the thick patch of trees near the spot, and pictured the short feeder-road, leading from both right and left, which led to the open gates of the park and to the road which ran up to the Hall. If he slowed down to look now, and the other car had pulled off the road in the hope of fooling him, the men in it would know he was looking for them; at the moment they couldn't be sure.

He saw the signpost to Foley Hall. Even at night the dilapidated white and black paint showed up. The tower was out of sight from here. He caught a glimpse of something black and shiny among the trees, and was quite sure that it was the other car. His heart began to pound. He scorched past without slacking speed, and if he were right and the men in the car were longing for him to pass, they would be slapping themselves on the back. The trouble at night was the glow of headlights in the sky, they could be seen from such a long way off.

There were the trees, a wide avenue which led into Foley Village; these would hide the headlights. They shone like silver for a few moments, and Roger saw what he had forgotten; a sharp turn to the right. That would help, too. So would a lay-by on the other side of the road, offering ample room to turn. He swung across to it, keeping the lights on; the longer they glowed in the sky, the better. He turned the car in swift, smooth movements, while breathing very hard. He switched off the headlights, and started back. The side lights gave only a faint glow, and it was difficult driving; he had to slow down to forty miles an hour when he wanted to be doing eighty. The journey to the feeder roads seemed to take five times as long as it had coming. He could see nothing, could hear nothing except the sound of his own car, and soon he would have to switch the engine off. He did so. The car slowed down, but ran on for longer than he had hoped; there must be a downwards slope here.

When would the police start out from Arncott; what would they do when they got the police constable's warning?

The signpost loomed up before he expected it, after all, and he actually had to brake. He could just make out the side of the road, the hard surface pale, dark where the grass was. He turned into it, and saw a light.

It was no more than a hundred yards away.

He switched off even his sidelights, and got out, careful not to close the door. His car blocked the road, but that didn't matter. There was no car at the spot where he had seen it, so it had been moved on. He saw the light again, a twinkle through the hedge, and against the grey sky he could see the towering blackness of Foley's Folly.

Someone was carrying a torch, and flashing it about.

Roger came upon an open gateway, and only a few yards inside a field, the other car. He banged his knee against the bumper, and winced. He stared at the torchlight, and saw the beam first pointing towards the ground and then towards the brick wall of the Folly.

He thought he saw the figure of a man outlined against it; then the light and the man disappeared. The going was difficult, reminding him of the hillside, and the haste made him keep stumbling. He had no doubt that he had come upon part of the mystery, but did not try to guess beyond that. He was gasping for breath, and yet trying not to make much noise.

He heard a bang; as of a door, opening and swinging back.

He tried to run. The meadowland deadened the sound of his footsteps but made it almost impossible to keep his balance. He stumbled, and his ankle turned over painfully. For a moment he stopped, wincing, standing on his left leg, holding his right foot off the ground. If he had sprained that ankle—

He tested it; it hurt, but there was no serious sprain. He went on a little more slowly, then saw a light again, against a small window of the Folly; a window about on a level with his head.

So they were going up the spiral staircase.

He glanced behind him, towards Arncott, but no lights in the sky promised other cars on the way. He was in this on his own. It was a tense moment, and he was brushed with fear, for if he had found the killers, they would not hesitate to kill again.

Why should they come here? Why go up—

'My God!' he exclaimed, and everything he remembered about the Folly came vividly to his mind. If these men had Mabel Tree with them, the one witness known to be in George Ansell's favour, they might be going to throw her over, to fake a suicide. He actually shouted: '*You there!*' as he reached the wall of the building, but his voice did not travel far, and the moment he had called out he knew that it could be a fatal mistake.

He found the door, open.

There was no light, and he crept in, finding his way by touch. He heard sounds: a kind of scuffling and heavy footsteps. As he reached the foot of the stairs, he knew that if they were carrying the woman up, it would explain their slow progress.

He kept a hand against the wall, and began to walk up, on his toes. He dared hardly breathe. The noises were plain enough above him; footsteps, very uneven; rustling, as men brushed against the wall; and heavy breathing. He had heard how many steps there were here, but couldn't remember. Over a hundred, anyhow, and he had climbed more than twenty steps. The others must be forty or fifty above him, so they were getting near the top.

Then a piercing sound came from above his head; a high-pitched scream.

'*Let me go!*'

There was a pause in the scuffling and the footsteps, and then another scream, with no words, a high-pitched cry of terror, telling him that a woman was there, telling him that she knew what the men were going to do.

A man rasped: 'Keep her quiet.'

'Don't mark—'

'To hell with marking her!'

'She can scream her head off, it won't hurt us. Don't let her fall.'

The screaming was becoming lower-pitched, as if the woman was losing both breath and hope, but in the seconds which had passed Roger had gained another ten steps. He would not hurry too much, for he must not get out of breath, and must take the men by surprise.

They were killers; they were going to kill this woman, and they would unhesitatingly kill him. He ought to have brought a spanner from the car; well, he hadn't. The screaming stopped, but he could hear the woman's heavy breathing as well as the other sounds, now. He thought he was probably making two steps to every one that the men were taking. The screaming had died away completely, and was replaced by a hopeless sobbing, as if the prisoner knew that there was nothing she could do to save herself.

Then, the footsteps stopped.

He judged that the men were twenty steps above him, and he heard them say, breathlessly:

'Shine the torch.'

'Gimme a chance.'

Roger saw the reflected glow of the torch-light, and felt sure that he was no more than twenty paces below them. The light seemed very bright in the darkness. He quickened his pace, as one of the men said:

'There's the door.'

'Open it.'

'Hold her.'

'A few bruises won't—'

'Please don't throw me over, please don't,' the woman begged, in a strange voice in which the words seemed to run into one another. 'Please don't kill me. I won't say anything, I promise not to say a word, please don't kill me. Oh, God, please don't let them kill me. God help me, save me. Oh, God, I know I've done the wrong thing, I know I shouldn't have been unfaithful to Fred, but help me, help me now, please God—'

A gust of wind came in; so the door was open.

'Let's get it over,' one of the men said.

'God, don't let them kill me!'

Roger called in a clear voice: 'That's enough. Drop her and put up your arms.'

He heard the startled gasp from the two men as he stood just out of sight, weaponless. He heard heavy breathing, before the woman began to scream again, as if hope had driven her over the borderline of madness.

'Drop her, and mind her head,' Roger ordered, and turned his head and spoke as if to someone below him. 'Keep close behind me, Jack.'

There was another gasp of sound, followed by a thud, as if the woman had been dropped.

Roger would have to show himself, and the moment the couple saw him they would know that he had no weapon, and was on his own. The light was still on, and he guessed that it was shining downwards. If he could put that light out it would give him a better chance. He could see the corner of the wall; the men must be on the platform, just out of sight.

If he could put that light out—

He heard a sharp rapping sound, as of a heel on stone, and

then the light went out. Men moved. He flattened himself
against the wall as they came. He knew exactly what was in
their minds, that they had taken what seemed to them the only
chance. But when no shooting came, they would realize that
they had been fooled. He put out a foot and one man pitched
against it and thudded against the wall, then slipped down two
or three steps. The torch shone out, straight into Roger's
eyes, blinding him. All he could do was to throw himself forward at the man holding the torch. He leapt, and felt a
tremendous blow in the pit of the stomach. Pain seared
through him. He almost collapsed, and was banged sickeningly
against the wall. The light was still on, covering his face,
dazzling him. He covered his face with his folded arms, and as
he did so felt a savage blow on his right forearm; his arm
went numb. He kicked out, as a man called from below:

'You all right?'

'Got to fix this so-and-so,' the man with Roger said roughly.
'If he gets away—'

'Don't use your knife!' shouted the man from below, the
man whom Roger had tripped; and with the cry came livid
fear. Roger thought he saw the glint of a knife, could imagine
it being driven upwards into his body, turned and tried to hurl
himself upwards. Then he made out the figure of a girl or
woman ahead of him, and thought that she was in the act of
throwing. He felt a sharp pain in his shoulder, not agonizing
but enough to make him wince. Something struck the wall, a
man staggered, there was a metallic sound, as if the knife had
dropped.

A man said viciously: 'Why, you little bitch—'

The man from below screeched: 'There's someone coming,
there's a light! Let's get away from here!'

*   *   *

Someone was coming.

*   *   *

Roger's head was going round and round, and his right arm still felt numb, but he had a few moments to collect himself, moments while his more dangerous assailant was standing still, startled by the warning. Then came the sound of a motor-cycle engine, and beyond it the sound of a car. Roger saw the man who had tried to kill him, a strange misshapen figure in the torch-light; and as the other turned to run down the stairs, Roger shot out a leg. The man tripped.

The woman cried:

'Don't go after him, don't!'

She was holding Roger's arm, and pulling. The man staggered but did not fall. The one at the foot of this flight of steps was already out of sight, his footsteps clattering down the stone stairs. Outside, a beam of light was weaving about the meadows, and the motor-cycle was coming much nearer; but there was no sign of car lights in spite of the other engine. Roger saw his assailant jump the stairs and go out of sight. The woman still clung to him, as if terrified of being left alone, but she need not have worried; he hadn't the strength left to go chasing after the man.

He gasped: 'Door, let me get to the door.' He staggered up three steps, and they seemed to be twice as tall as those he had stepped up earlier. Cold wind cut through the open door. He staggered out on to the platform, seeing the wavering light perhaps fifty yards away. The wind stung his forehead and neck as he gripped the iron railing at waist height, and called:

'Be careful! Armed men!'

The woman was by his side.

'*Be careful!*' she screeched. '*They're armed.*'

Then the two men seemed to burst from the door of Foley's Folly, and the beam of light fell upon them. Roger had no idea who was there, no idea what chance the motor-cyclist would have in a fight; he almost wished the man would dodge to one side.

The direction of the light changed, and it shone right into

the faces of the two men. Roger had a distorted view, but knew that he would recognize them again. The motor-cyclist must have a clear full-face view. Then the light was switched off, and there was pitch darkness. But in the distance there was much more light, as if several cars were coming along the main road.

Police?

Roger muttered: 'I've got to get down there, got to stop them—'

'Don't go,' the woman begged. 'Don't you, you'll be too late.'

He knew he would be too late, anyhow; if the motor-cyclist was attacked, he would have little chance.

The lights shone out again, and the two men were just in sight, stumbling over the uneven land towards the parked car; it shone faintly in the end of the beam of light.

Then the motor-cyclist bellowed: 'You haven't got a flickin' chance, you bastards.'

That was Percy Snell; and the 'motor-cycle' was his Vespa.

*   *   *

Roger shouted: 'Percy!'

'Who the hell—' began Snell, and stared upwards, his face just visible. 'Strewth! *Handsome!*'

'Can you stop them?'

'They're stopped,' Snell bellowed, with supreme confidence. 'They won't have a chance. What are you doing up there?'

The two men were nearer the car, and its engine was running. The light from the headlamps of the approaching cars enabled Roger to see much more than he had before. The cars were only half a mile away now, and there were four or five of them. Then there were sounds as of doors slamming. Roger thought: 'They'll get off, how the hell did they start that engine?' Then he heard the engine roar and the car move.

Snell shouted. 'They won't get far on four flat tyres,

Handsome! With a bit of luck we'll have 'em in ten minutes.' He switched the light towards the car as it crawled forward. Snell was laughing; Snell usually was when things were going right. The approaching cars would be here in two or three minutes, and the woman's assailants hadn't a chance. What a way to catch them! Roger stood leaning against the rail, just aware of the fact that Mabel Tree was pressing against him, clutching his arm with her two hands.

He saw the shapes of the two killers get out of the car and begin to run towards the road.

He thought in swift alarm: 'My car's there!'

'Percy!' he yelled. 'My car's on the road. Stop them!'

'Gorblimey!' Snell called up. 'What do you want to do, give 'em a sporting chance?' He jumped on to his Vespa, and started the engine. Roger heard the two men running, felt the tension of the woman by his side, knew that the two killers would need only seconds to start the engine of his car even without a key; a piece of wire or a master key would serve.

Snell was wobbling towards the road, the others within a hundred yards, when Roger saw his own car's lights go on. The car swung along the main road towards Foley Village.

CHAPTER XVI

ALIBI FOR ONE

'WE'LL SOON pick 'em up, don't you worry,' Percy Snell said. He sounded as if he did not know whether to be angry or amused. 'You couldn't have done any more than you did, that's one certain thing. Okay if I leave you here and go and see what's cooking?'

'Yes. What were you doing out there?' Roger asked.

'Just looking round. I wondered if there'd be any nocturnal visitors at the Hall tonight,' Snell answered. 'I heard the car come, and coasted down the hill to see what it was all about. Lucky thing for you you brought a good man with you, eh, Mr Gale?' He grinned at John Gale, who was in the kitchen of his house, with Roger. They had been here only a few minutes, but already Roger's coat was off, the bloodstained shirt-sleeve was rolled up, and Daphne Gale was bathing the cut.

Mabel Tree was in the front room, with Kathleen Russell and Lionel Foley. Roger now knew that Foley had been persuaded to stay to dinner, and had lingered. A local constable was in the front room with them; and the last Roger had seen of Mabel Tree was of a pathetic little figure, with great rounded eyes and bent shoulders, recovered from her terror, remarkably composed in view of what had happened to her, but now looking into a bleak future. He would never forget the way she had hurled that brick at the man who would have killed him.

Daphne said: 'It isn't very deep, I shouldn't think it will need stitches. What do you think, John?'

Gale studied the cut.

'I'd put some of that penicillin cream on, the stuff I used when I cut my leg last month, and bandage it. Easy enough place to bandage. How do you feel, Mr West?'

'I'm all right.'

'He looks as if he wants a good night's sleep,' Daphne said, with that downrightness which was so unexpected in a woman who looked so fragile. 'I'll get a bandage, you keep a cold cloth pressed on there while I'm gone.'

'Right.'

Daphne went hurrying.

Gale said: 'Move over here and sit down, you look pretty groggy.'

'A nip of brandy will put me right.' Roger said. 'There's a flask in my hip pocket. I'll hold the compress, you pour me a nip.' Gale let him take the wet cloth, and got out the flask, which he had last used for Lionel Foley. The brandy seemed to do Roger good immediately, although for a few seconds his head swam. When that was over he felt much better, and believed that there was even colour in his lips. Gale lit a cigarette for him, and he said: 'Thanks. Wonder if they've got the swine yet.'

'Your man seems pretty confident.'

'He was born optimistic,' Roger said, and did not add that Snell was still Detective Inspector because of his often unreasoning optimism; everything would always work out all right, in Percy Snell's opinion. This time he might be right. Three Arncott police cars had gone after the two men, and warnings had been radioed to all towns en route; by now there would be blocks on all roads leading from Arncott. There was a chance that the men had managed to get to Reading, and switch cars; that was their only real hope of escaping.

Roger had talked to Hooper by radio, and Hooper was expecting him at the police station about half past ten; it was now nearly ten o'clock.

Gale said: 'I know it's none of my business, but where does Mabel Tree come into this?'

Roger said: 'I suppose you'll have to know eventually, but I wish I could keep her out of it.' That was wishing for the moon. 'Tree's one of your lads, isn't he?'

'Just.'

'Eh?'

'He's a damned knowledgeable man with horses but that's about all,' Gale answered. 'He causes more bad feeling among the men than anyone else I know. If it weren't for Mabel, I'd have fired him months ago. But she's a Cartwright, and Cartwrights have been working here for about five generations.'

Roger said: 'She's something else too – George Ansell's alibi for last night.'

Gale actually moved back two paces.

'It can't be!'

'It's true,' Roger asseverated.

'Good lord! A Cartwright and an Ansell—'

Roger said: 'You'll know by the morning. We'll never keep this out of the newspapers, so you might as well know now that two men were going to throw her from Foley's Folly, in a fake suicide. That would take away Ansell's alibi. If she thought there was a risk of the association being found out she would be in the mood for suicide, it wouldn't look remarkable. So it was cold-bloodedly worked out.'

'I'll say it was! But I'd no idea,' Gale marvelled. 'I know most of the tit-bits of scandal connected with our chaps, you'd be surprised how much there is, but those two – good God!'

Roger said: 'And I take it that Tree will give her hell.'

'He's the kind who would like to take a whip to her, and—' Gale broke off, and then added in a strangled voice: 'I knew she was pretty miserable, no one could live with Fred Tree for long without feeling fed up. I wonder what on earth brought her and George Ansell together.' He fell silent when he heard his wife's footsteps as she came from the foot of the stairs. 'We'll soon have something on that wound. My wife's quite trustworthy, by the way, but I'll understand if you don't want her to know yet.'

'What mustn't I know?' Daphne came in, sharp-voiced.

Roger said: 'In confidence, Mrs Gale, this.' He told her

because he wanted to find out whether, like Mrs Hooper, she knew more than her husband, and as she bandaged his arm she kept glancing at him; he wondered what went on behind those clear, china-blue eyes. She pinned the bandage, and then said briskly:

'I knew there was someone, but I didn't know who it was. Mabel used to be a maid here, and any of the other lads would have let her keep her job on, but not Fred Tree. And he's out at the Arncott Arms most nights. If ever a man—' She broke off. 'Well, I suppose I shouldn't condone it. I've just glanced in at her, she looks as if she'll pass out if someone doesn't say something to help her.'

Roger said: 'Cut that sleeve off my shirt, will you, and I'll put a coat on and go and have a word with her.'

'There's no need to cut it, I'll wash that blood out in cold water,' Daphne offered. 'John, pop upstairs and get one of your old shirts, will you – one of those with the large necks, he's thicker there than you are.' She waited until her husband had gone, and then asked Roger very quietly: 'Can you keep this from Mabel's husband for the night?' When Roger didn't answer, she went on sharply: 'That girl must have some rest. She's had one terrible shock after another. I'm not sure that we oughtn't to let a doctor see her. If you make her face her husband tonight, I'll—'

Roger said with a grin: 'Last thing I'd do. I was wondering if there was any way of stopping Tree from ever finding out. We're not likely to charge George Ansell yet, now that this alibi has turned up. We might have to later, but I shouldn't think so, the two men who nearly killed Mrs Tree are almost certainly our men. They probably have associates down here, but that's about all. I can't see George Ansell being both crook's associate and employer's stooge. We'll tell Tree part of the story, and if his wife can stay here for the night – on doctor's orders, say – we'd have some time to play with.'

'So you are a human being,' Daphne observed. 'Sorry if I

snapped. She can stay here as long as you like, of course. Who'll see Tree?'

'I will,' said Roger.

John Gale came in, carrying a white shirt with a collar attached. Daphne watched quite impersonally as Roger changed. Roger went out, passing the front room where Kathleen Russell and Lionel Foley were sitting and talking, with radio music in the background; he caught a glimpse of Foley's heavily bandaged foot. His own mind was working more rationally, and he was beginning to understand some problems which had been resolved and the new ones which had been presented. In a way, the sense of urgency had gone – the sense of danger. Those two men, strangers to him, were almost certainly strangers to the district. If they were caught and if they talked, there wouldn't be much mystery.

Roger entered the small room where a local sergeant, Dayton, was standing, and Mabel Tree was sitting back in a comfortable armchair, her eyes closed, a tea tray by her side. A cup of tea was half full on the tray. She opened her eyes when she heard someone come in, and when she saw who it was, sat up quickly.

'Take it easy,' Roger said, and smiled. 'How are you feeling?'

'I suppose I'm all right, and – and I can't thank you enough for—'

'What you did when he was using that knife cancels out anything you owe me,' Roger declared, and sat on the edge of a chair, looking at her. 'All right, Sergeant, wait outside, will you?' He glanced at Daphne Gale, and said: 'Sorry.' She grimaced, and went out too, closing the door.

The room was comfortably furnished and pleasantly warm. There were photographs of horses on one wall, a dozen or more of them, and each photograph was signed by owner or jockey.

'Now, Mrs Tree,' Roger said, 'we know you've some acute personal problems and we want to help all we can. You're to stay here tonight, under doctor's orders, and that will give us time to see how much can be kept out of the newspapers. If we can keep the whole story out, we will. But you must answer my questions frankly – I've got to know the whole truth.'

'I'll tell you the truth,' she promised him, and there was a film of tears in her eyes.

'Good. How long has this association with George Ansell been going on?'

'For about six months, I suppose.'

'When did it start?'

'Well, it was a funny thing, really. I usually go to Reading once a fortnight, my husband doesn't like me going more often, and it was my day out, if you know what I mean. I love big towns, especially on market days. And I was at the market one day when George was there, buying some rubber boots and some gardening things; he always buys in the lowest market. We had a cup of tea together – we used to know each other at school, see – and, well, one thing led to another. I told him how it was between me and Fred, and he told me that he had an idea about that, he never did like Fred. And – well, I happened to be going to the pictures, and he offered to take me. That's all there was to it, sir. Then we arranged to meet at the market the next month, and it was in the summer. We – we didn't go to the pictures, we – we had a boat out, and—'

There was no need to turn the screw.

'All right, Mrs Tree,' Roger said quietly, and knew that now she had told someone it would help; like pus freed from a festering wound. 'When did you last see George?'

'Why, last night.'

'Did you meet in Reading as usual?'

'Yes, in a way – George said he couldn't get in for the afternoon, there'd been some kind of trouble at the Hall, and he'd been taken off his gardening. If he'd taken his usual half-day off it would have looked funny, so he came out to join me for the evening, that's all. I – I've invented a friend in Reading, and so long as I only have one day out a month Fred doesn't care what time I get home. Not that it matters much to him, I'm only a skivvy—' She broke off, and closed her eyes; tears forced their way through. 'But I suppose I shouldn't say anything about him – *I'm* the one who's in the wrong. Mr West, I don't know what my husband will say when he finds out. I just don't know. I wouldn't be surprised if he doesn't kill me.'

'He won't kill you, and he won't harm you,' Roger assured her. 'We've ways of making sure of that.' They were just words, but offered a kind of comfort. 'What time was George in Reading?'

'He arrived about eight o'clock.'

'What time did he leave?'

'Well, we left in the car, he always gives me a lift back in the dark evenings. I get off on the other side of Arncott, and catch the Reading bus from there. Then it looks as if I've come from some friends of mine who have a cottage out that way. We've been ever so careful,' Mabel went on, and swallowed hard. 'We felt we had to be, although we've hated it.'

'What time did you leave Reading last night?'

'It was about half past nine, as usual.'

'What time did you get to Arncott?'

'I caught the bus that gets to the Clock Tower at a quarter to eleven,' Mabel answered. 'It was later than usual; I like to get home before Fred's back from the pub, but, I'm not always. He's sometimes a bit nasty about it, but I don't take any notice of that.'

'What time did you catch the bus?'

'I suppose it was half past ten; it takes a quarter of an hour from that bus stop.'

'How long had you waited there?'

'Only a couple of minutes,' said Mabel Tree. 'In fact I was afraid we were going to miss it; George had to step on the gas to pass the bus and put me down without it being too noticeable.'

'How many people were on the bus?'

'It was nearly full.'

'Was there anyone you know on it?'

'Oh, several people.'

'If that's true, then you can keep George out of serious trouble,' Roger said.

'Oh, I swear it's true!'

'Right!' Roger stood up, glad to see that she was much more relaxed. 'We may not need this as formal evidence, Mrs Tree, if we don't it may never come out. I don't quite know how we're going to explain things away to your husband, but we can worry about that later.' He leaned forward and rested a hand on her shoulder. 'The doctor will be here in a few minutes. He'll give you a sedative, and I'll see you in the morning. So far as George is concerned, I don't think you've much to fear.'

'That's really all that matters,' Mabel said, very quietly. 'I'm beginning to wonder if it wouldn't be best to tell Fred the truth, after all. It's got to come out sooner or later, and even if George wasn't in love with me I couldn't go on with Fred much longer. If you knew what it was like when he comes home the worse for drink, he—'

'I can imagine,' Roger said, and then heard a ring at the front door. 'That'll be the doctor,' he added, and went out.

*   *   *

It was the doctor; and in five minutes Mabel Tree was in a spare bedroom; in fifteen she would be asleep.

Roger had a word with Lionel Foley, and carried away that impression of an understanding between him and Kathleen Russell which he didn't yet comprehend; there were still many things he did not yet begin to understand. How long had he been down here? About fourteen hours. He grinned. He felt numbness in his arm, and knew that Daphne Gale was quite right; he needed a rest, if not for the reason she had in mind. He needed to be needle-sharp in this affair, and he wasn't; the struggle in the Folly had been too tense and taken too much out of him. He had an uneasy feeling that he had missed something obvious, but couldn't think what. He felt as if he were at half pressure, as he was driven by one of Hooper's men towards the station; and half pressure wouldn't be of any use on this job.

Unless those two men were caught soon.

The thing on Roger's mind concerned the two men; and some things fell into position. They weren't locals, or they would have used the Cut, as he had been advised to, instead of the longer way round. So they were from outside. London? If so, they knew a surprising amount about local people and local circumstances. They had known about George Ansell and Mabel Tree, for instance, when very few people in the village or in Arncott had. That was really remarkable. So they had made a dead set at Ansell, trying to implicate him – and trying to implicate Lady Foley?

What about Colonel Madden, who hovered on the fringe of the mystery, neither in nor out of it; Colonel Madden, who was always hard up, who had sent that piece of gossip up to the *Racecourse* and in a way started everything? There was another significant fact. If the attack on the horse had been the main factor, then the murders were subsidiary. Some-one must have been wanting, almost waiting, to kill Silver Monarch, and been poised ready to seize the chance. It hadn't happened because Lady Foley had threatened to kill her son's horse. Her threat had been the excuse for pulling of the trigger, but the gun had been loaded.

On this theory, someone had been lying in wait to kill that world-beating horse.

Why kill Silver Monarch?

Once he had the motive for that, he might have the full explanation.

Was there any sense in forcing his mind like this? He might arrive at the station and find that the two men had been caught; if they had, then questioning would soon reveal the truth. But his mind was too restless, and he could not shut out the questions which crowded in. He had once considered Lady Foley as the instigator, and when Ansell had been a suspect, that had been reasonable, but these outsiders – would Lady Foley pay outsiders? It was almost certain that she would not, he told himself. And would she connive at crimes which so obviously pointed a finger of guilt at her?

Look at the facts.

Attempts had been made to implicate Lady Foley and George Ansell? Why? Enmity towards one or both?

'I want to know two things,' Roger said, sotto-voce. 'Why did young Foley try to burn that car, and why did someone actually do it? And is there anyone who hates Lady Foley so much that they'd try to frame her?'

The driver asked, startled: 'What's that, sir?'

'Sorry. Forget it.'

'Couldn't help catching what you said,' the driver told Roger after he had allowed a moment for the words to sink in. 'I don't know about the trouble with the old Austin, but I do know a bit about Lady Foley and the family. I've lived here all my life, be a funny thing if I didn't know something, wouldn't it?'

'Go on.'

'Never been any love lost between her and her brother, Colonel Madden,' the driver said. 'He always wanted to train at the stables up at the Hall, but she wouldn't have any of it. She kicked him out of the Hall into the cottage, too, and he hates her guts. He's taken every chance he's ever had of a bit of spite – no doubt about that, sir.'

'Ah,' said Roger. 'The Colonel.'

Madden hadn't lost a second in putting out the scandal paragraph which had started all this, and he was a man with cause to hate. But why should he or anyone else implicate George Ansell?

Suddenly, Roger felt as if he had been kicked.

One man certainly had cause to hate George.

Fred Tree.

CHAPTER XVII

MOTIVES

HOOPER WAS sitting in his starkly modern office, like a restive bull in a china shop. He was on the telephone, his coat was off and his shirt-sleeves rolled up, for the office was stiflingly warm. Snell was sitting at the smaller desk, with a bottle of beer and a plate in front of him, there were the crumbs of sandwiches on the plate. He gave a thumbs down sign.

Roger closed the door quietly.

'Oh, Gawd,' Hooper growled. 'What do they want, a magnet?' He slammed the receiver down and glared up at Roger as if whatever was wrong was the Yard man's fault. 'Those two swine beat a police block the other side of Reading; not much doubt it was the pair we're after. Your car's a wreck.'

Roger said: 'Thanks.'

'Don't thank *me*. Like making a present of ignition keys to a couple of killers?'

Roger put his hand in his pocket, took out his keys and tossed them to the desk. Hooper grabbed them before they touched the polished wood.

'My keys,' said Roger.

'Oh, all right, no need to scratch my desk,' said Hooper. 'Am I sore! Another two minutes and we'd have had them.' He scowled. 'Well, how're you?' he inquired at last. 'You don't look much the worse for it.'

'I'll get by.'

'One thing about it, we do know that the swine come from outside the area. Snell's given a description of them and I'd know if they were from Arncott or Reading. Wonder who the hell's putting them up to this? Two murders and two damn' nearlies. That right Mabel Tree saved your wife from being a widow?'

'Near enough.'

'All wives have to carry some burdens,' grunted Hooper, and the crack made him smile, although lugubriously. 'Sit down, Handsome, and take that smirk off your face.' He started up. 'Smirk, that's about right. What are you looking so pleased about?'

'Bert, there were the two witnesses earlier today who said they'd seen Lady Foley driving that Austin about the time that Syd Cartwright vanished. One was Tree.'

'Right.'

'He drinks a lot at the local.'

'That's right.'

'The other witness to say Lady Foley was driving that car was a barman. At Tree's favourite pub, I wonder?'

Hooper was shaken into silence, and then gasped.

'Oh, Gawd, what have I done?' He leaned back and raised his arms, clenched his fists and hit them in a curious backwards beat against the wall. He looked positively ugly as he sat there, and Snell gaped at him, while holding a glass of beer close to his mouth.

'Yes, Tree's favourite pub, the Arncott Arms. Don't tell me. It would put Lady Foley inside, and it would put George Ansell in jug for the rest of his life. There's your motive for Tree to frame George – assuming he knows about George and his Mabel. Don't tell me. Tree.'

'Where is he?' Roger demanded.

'We sent him home, nearly an hour ago,' said Hooper. 'My God, he must have wondered what we sent for him for, he must wonder if we're on to him.' He snatched up a telephone receiver, and bellowed: 'Give me Frobisher ... Froby? ... Send a car along to Copse Road again, have it watched each end, make sure that Fred Tree doesn't do a moonlight flit. Yes, I said Fred Tree. Make sure he's home, too ... Goddammit I don't care how you find out, all I want is you to make sure he's there and stays there! If he looks like having a little jaunt, ask him why, and bring him along here.'

He banged down the receiver.

'Not that I believe in jumping to conclusions,' he said more blandly. 'Fred Tree. Could be. He's someone to question, anyhow. If he has known all about the *affaire* between his wife and George, then it would explain a lot. He's the biggest know-all in the district, and he's so full of Number One he looks like bursting sometimes. If he thought his wife would shame him by running off with another man—' He snatched up the receiver again. 'Gimme Frobisher ... Well, send a man after him; tell him we want Tree back here, quick.' He slammed the receiver down again. 'That right, Handsome?'

Roger said, very slowly: 'I don't know.' His tone was so unexpected that he startled both Snell and Hooper; Snell gulped down the last of his beer and lowered the glass abruptly because Roger was staring at him.

'Now what?' Hooper demanded.

Roger said: 'Ted Cartwright saw the murder, and was killed. Syd Cartwright saw one man, and was killed. Mabel and I nearly stopped the men escaping tonight, and they were prepared to kill us. Anyone who can give us a lead to them gets killed. It's as ugly as sin. Percy, you stay here. You *saw* them tonight, and if that's passed back to their associates here, you could be on the list. Bert, Fred Tree is probably involved. If he is, he can name these fellows, and can possibly name the local associates – including that barman. Everyone else who could point a finger at the murderers has been killed or attacked.'

Hooper stood up, very slowly.

'Frobisher will be there by now,' he said. 'If he finds anything wrong, we'll soon know.' He didn't lift the receiver, but glanced at Snell. 'That's right about you, too?'

'*I'm* all right,' Snell retorted bluffly. 'No one's going to scare me into staying indoors. But this Tree—'

He broke off.

There was a tension in the office for half a minute; and silence made the tension worse. It was difficult to think of anything except the message which might soon be coming; either there would be word of trouble at Tree's house, or news that Frobisher was on the way.

The telephone bell rang.

Hooper snatched up the receiver.

'Hooper ...'

He paused; he opened his mouth as if to shout, but no sound came; he said:

'Flash a call out for him to all radio cars, I'll see to the general call.' He banged down the receiver and then flicked on the inter-office machine. 'Sparks ... Put out a general call for Frederick Tree; you know what he looks like. London as well as Reading and Oxford – everywhere, if it comes to that. Have Sammy Links the barman at the Arncott Arms brought in for questioning, too. I'll talk to him. Ta.' He replaced the receiver, and announced harshly: 'He's cleared out – packed a bag and gone,' he said. 'A neighbour saw him driving off, but there's no certainty about what car it was. Well, how about that? He packed a case, Frobisher says – drawers and cupboards all mussed up, no doubt he's skipped. Must have put the wind up him when we pulled him in for questioning. And I should have put that two and two together before you did. *Tree*. Hates George Ansell's guts, hates the Foleys, nasty piece of work all round. But he wouldn't do a thing like this on his own, he's working for someone else, no doubt about that. He – my Gawd! Someone unlocked that door in the stable gates to let the killers into Gale's yard. Tree was around that night, as we know. How about it, Handsome?'

'We want Tree, and we want the other two, but mostly we want whoever's behind it all,' Roger said. 'It's almost certainly someone in the neighbourhood. It's also possible that Tree's gone into hiding with that someone. Foley Hall is watched, we'll know if he goes there. Can you have a messenger sent out to warn the guards to look out for him?'

'Good as done.'

'And Colonel Madden,' Roger said. 'Is his cottage being watched?'

'No.'

'Watch it.'

'Good as done.' Hooper's hand was hovering over the telephone.

'Gale's stables are being watched, but what about the house?'

'*What?*'

'There's the history of bitter antagonism between the racing stables and Lady Foley. There's the evidence of hostility between Daphne Gale and Lady Foley. Percy, did you ever find out if young Lionel Foley and Kathleen Russell are old acquaintances?'

'I asked the Yard again, haven't had any report yet. They still aren't sure about Foley's alibi last night.'

'See if the night boys know anything more. Got any reports on Lionel Foley's associates in London?'

'No.'

'Doesn't anyone at the Yard move on this case?' Roger demanded.

Hooper was saying into the telephone. '... have a motor-cyclist warn the guards at Foley House to look out for Fred Tree, send two men to watch Colonel Madden's cottage, looking out for Tree, checking on anyone else who's there – have two men outside Gale's house, and two at the back, in addition to the stables ... yes, I said Gale's house, you're not deaf. Right.'

Snell was staring at Roger as he held a receiver to his ear; he had asked for the Yard, and was holding on. Hooper had fallen silent. His telephone rang sharply, and he snatched it up.

'Hooper ...'

There was a pause, and then he grunted and slapped the receiver down.

'Madden's at the Hall with his sister,' he said, 'and young Foley's just arrived there, with Kathleen Russell, who drove him home. I had a man watching him like you said, but he's properly crippled. Nothing else has happened up at the house. No canoodling. Handsome—'

'Yes?'

'You scare me sometimes. Gale couldn't—.

'Anyone could be involved and you know it,' Roger said. 'The only certain thing is that Ted and Syd Cartwright saw someone who dared not risk being identified. I like what I know of the Gales, too, I'd like pounds for the number of criminals who are quite pleasant as people. Percy, sure you don't mind risking your neck?'

'Think nothing of it,' Snell grinned, and then pressed the telephone against his ear. 'Here's the Yard, half a mo'.'

The others watched him tensely as he listened; suddenly he waved his hand, and began to repeat what he heard.

'Slower, Micky ... Kathleen Russell works for Hackensmith and Bordy; of course I know they're big bookmakers ... Colonel Madden owes them a packet, too, how much? ... Can't you be more specific? ... Okay, around ten thousand quid and I know it's not a certified statement of accounts, don't give me that ... Lionel Foley's credit stopped and they're dunning him ... Why the hell didn't we get all this hours ago? ... Okay, anything else? ... Oh, we know that Corrison and old Lord F. hated each other, but the old boy's been dead ten years ... Right, ta.' He banged down the receiver, and leaned on the small desk with both hands, head thrust forward, looking at them rather like a big bear. 'You got that,' he said. 'Hackensmith and Bordy don't like favourites winning, they never did. Been a lot of rumours about them being behind a doping ring – even the job I was on years ago. Anyone know about Daphne Gale's sister being connected with them?'

Hooper growled: 'No reason why we should know. This

damned case has moved so fast the skids are under us all the time. Going to talk to her, Handsome?'

'As soon as I can. How bad was the feeling between Corrison, the owner of Silver Monarch, and the late Lord Foley?'

'One of those feuds,' Hooper said. 'Foley's horses were always being beaten by Corrison's.'

'Feuds run in families,' Roger said.

'My God! And Colonel Madden took over that one!'

'I'm going to talk to Colonel Madden right away,' Roger went on. 'How long has his credit been stopped?'

'It hasn't. He gives them a lot of inside information and they allow him credit for betting.'

'Tell you something else,' Snell said, still crouching. 'Hackensmith and Bordy own the *Racecourse* and a lot of other racing journals – and they have their scandal and gossip spies out among owners, trainers, jockeys, the lot. Take it from me, they'd prefer Silver Monarch dead to alive, and the one definite contact they have down here is Madden.'

'Who would have his touts among the stable lads,' Roger said swiftly.

'Yep.'

'Tree's been flashing his money about,' Hooper put in. 'Tree and Madden are fairly thick.'

'John Gale told me that Tree's known to give information to newspapermen,' Roger said in a clipped voice.

'The Cartwrights would recognize him,' Hooper put in, 'and he could always have access to Lady Foley's Austin. Blood being thicker than water, Lionel Foley would want to get rid of all evidence that his uncle had driven that car. Colonel Madden driving the Austin wouldn't really be noticeable – he so often does.'

'Yes.'

'Let's get a search warrant,' Hooper growled, and then the telephone bell rang. He snatched up the receiver. 'Hooper.'

There was a pause, and his face positively blanched.

'Gawd!' he exclaimed. 'Yes, handle it yourself.' He put down the receiver, and looked tensely at the others. 'Sammy Links, our barman, was found in the yard of the Arncott Arms. Head bashed in. Tree went straight to the pub from here, but left after a couple of drinks. Come on.'

CHAPTER XVIII

THE COLONEL'S COTTAGE

POLICE GUARDS on duty seemed to be everywhere. As Roger and Snell were driven by Hooper in his Humber Hawk past the stables, there were the policemen outside the Gales' house as well as those outside the stables. The gates were closed, but the lights on inside the yard were much more powerful, and a glow of light spread towards the sky. Further on, there was a police patrol at the approach to Foley Hall. A policeman waved them down halfway up the private road, and when they branched off, towards the cottages, another waved them down with his torch.

Lights were on at the gardener's cottage, where the old man and his daughter would be sitting, the children would be in bed, and George Ansell's small room empty; but if things were what they seemed it would not be empty for long. There were no lights on at the Colonel's cottage, but again a policeman stepped out of the darkness and waved them down with his torch, while a second man stood by, to make sure that there was no trouble. The torch flashed into Hooper's face, and was swung away immediately.

'All quiet?' Hooper asked.

'Yes, sir.'

'Colonel Madden still at the Hall?'

'He's not come back here, sir.'

'Right. Keep your eyes peeled, I've a search warrant and I'm going into that cottage. Don't let anyone catch us bending.'

'No, sir.'

'How long have you been here?' Roger asked.

'Half an hour or so, sir.'

'Better have a man at the back; if Tree did come here

and is still alive, we'll flush him out,' Roger said. 'Percy, will you go?'

'You go with Inspector Snell, Goodison,' Hooper said; and in that dark, chilly night, Roger found himself remembering that Hooper was a damned good man: he knew all of his chaps by name, and had an easy manner with them; it was easy to believe that they would serve him with absolute loyalty.

Snell and the policeman went off.

'Give 'em two minutes,' Hooper said. 'Don't see any light, do you?'

'No.'

'Can't imagine his skulking in there without any light on; he'd want a candle, anyhow,' Hooper said. 'I've got a feeling that we're going to have a lot of trouble catching Tree. But if he can be made to talk ...' He went on muttering to himself as they approached the front door. He pushed it, but it was locked. 'Hope it's not bolted,' Hooper muttered, and began to fiddle with a skeleton key. Roger heard the sharp click as the lock went back. '*Quiet*,' breathed Hooper, and stood with the door ajar, listening; but there was not the faintest sound.

Hooper pushed the door wider open. It squeaked a little. They stood in the front room which opened straight into the garden, listening and hearing nothing.

'We'll have some light. Okay?'

'Yes,' Roger said.

Hooper put on a torch, found an electric switch, and pressed it down. A bright light filled the narrow room, showing an open door leading to a back room, and shining up the narrow flight of stairs which led upwards. There was the Victorian furniture, the photographs, the peeling wallpaper. A coal fire was out, in the grate, and an electric fire, dead and cold, stood by it.

There was no sound.

'I'll go upstairs,' Hooper said. 'You go and check with Snell, will you?'

Why shouldn't he give the orders?

'Right,' Roger said, and went towards the doorway leading to the back room, which would be the kitchen. It was, but it was not empty. Sitting back in a wooden armchair, head lolling grotesquely to one side, was Fred Tree.

Dead.

Fred must have been attacked from behind. He looked much as Ted Cartwright had, when he had first been found; much as the dead barman, too.

*   *   *

Roger stood staring; sickened.

Hooper called down: 'Nothing up here.' When Roger didn't answer, he came hurrying, his footsteps sounding clearly through the small cottage. Roger turned to look at him, and he stopped short.

'What's up?'

'We've found Fred Tree,' Roger answered, and forced himself to move. 'Let's have a quick look round, before we go across to the Hall.' He opened the back door and the light fell on Percy Snell. 'Percy, get over to the Hall and check with all our chaps outside – don't let Colonel Madden leave, either. If he tries to, he's to be held.'

'Tree here?'

'Good and dead, like the others,' Roger called, in a rasping voice.

*   *   *

They spent twenty minutes searching the cottage. The only things they found of immediate interest were typewritten copies of 'stories' which Colonel Madden had sent to *Racecourse* and other racing papers, letters from Hackensmith and Bordy about his debts, which had reached a total of eleven thousand and fifty-one pounds at the end of the previous month. But there was one other thing: a letter from the firm, asking for fullest details of Silver Monarch, details of gallops, training, the lads who looked after him, assessment of his capabilities; the Colonel had undoubtedly been keeping his masters closely informed.

* * *

There were several lights on at Foley Hall, each one downstairs. A car stood outside the side entrance, and Roger recognized it as Gale's car. Three policemen were on duty here, and Hooper spoke to them.

'Who's still inside?'

'No one's come out in the last half hour, sir. Lady Foley's there, Colonel Madden, Miss Russell and Lionel Foley. I'm not sure about the servants at the back entrance, sir, but I think they're all at Ansell's cottage.'

'Checked with the back door guard lately?'

'We have one man going round all the time, sir.'

'Good,' Hooper said. He stepped to the door and put his finger on the bell; he seemed to keep it there for a long time. Then footsteps sounded, sharply; that would be Lady Foley. There was something oddly incongruous about the thought of the owner of this great mansion coming to open her own front door because she had no staff on duty after eight o'clock at night.

It was Lady Foley.

'Good evening, my lady,' Hooper said. 'Sorry to worry you so late as this, but I would like to have a word with you and Mr Lionel.'

Lady Foley stared from him to Roger, as if she knew that Roger was really in command; he half expected her to protest, but she drew aside and said:

'I presume it is necessary, or you wouldn't be here.'

'It's essential,' Hooper said. 'Thank you, Lady Foley.' He took off his trilby. Roger followed him in, and Percy Snell brought up the rear.

'My son is with my brother and Miss Russell,' Lady Foley

stated: 'As you doubtless know, he can hardly hobble about. I can't ask him to come here.'

'We'll go to him,' Hooper said, and glanced at Roger as if realizing belatedly that he was usurping Roger's position. 'Do we want Miss Russell present, Mr West?'

'If this is a family matter—' Lady Foley began quickly, but stopped when she saw Roger staring at her intently; he meant to make her stop. He meant to puzzle the others as he stared at her, too. He meant to fray her nerves, knowing that she could not possibly be as calm and poised as she appeared to be.

Her voice grew sharp.

'What is it, Superintendent?'

'I asked you this morning if your son was in any difficulties. Why didn't you tell me that he was heavily in debt to a firm of bookmakers, and being dunned by them?'

She said: 'Apparently you have found that out for yourselves.'

'Is that another reason why you were so hostile towards him over the horse, Shoestring?'

'Is that relevant?'

'Acutely.'

'Yes, it was a reason,' Lady Foley admitted, and seemed to sag a little, as if she would gladly have leaned against the wall for support. 'He was ruining himself. This horse would only make the situation worse, not better. How much does he owe?' she added, and her voice sounded weary. 'Is it possible to pay—'

'Lady Foley, why did you set fire to your car this afternoon?'

She didn't answer; but the colour was fading from her cheeks, and there were two spots of bright red on them; that was all. Her eyes seemed very bright, as if she had a throbbing headache.

Roger repeated sharply: 'Well, why? What were you so anxious to destroy?'

She closed her eyes.

Hooper was staring at Roger, Percy was grinning all over his face.

'Lady Foley, unless you answer our questions, we shall be compelled to take you into Arncott for further questioning.'

She opened her eyes again, and there was anguish in them.

'I had seen bloodstains in the car,' she said, 'and wanted to destroy them. I realized that if they were found you would know for certain that Sydney Cartwright had been killed while in the car.'

'You know that witnesses testified that you were in that car this morning, don't you?'

'Yes.'

'Were you?'

'I was not.'

'Then who was?'

She didn't answer.

Roger said, very softly: 'What good do you think this delay will do, Lady Foley? There were bloodstains, and there was evidence that someone had driven the car – someone whose fingerprints you also wanted to destroy, and perhaps other evidence. Who drove that car after the stable lad was kidnapped? Who was driving it when he was slaughtered?'

She winced at the word.

'Who was it?' Roger rapped.

She said: 'It was Colonel Madden. My brother.' She closed her eyes for a moment again, and then seemed to draw herself up; she would never be anything but a small woman, but there was dignity and grace in the way she stood there; and pride, also. 'I have told you that only because it is obvious that you would have found it out sooner or later.' When Roger stood staring at her, she went on slowly: 'My son tried to destroy the car and the evidence, but you prevented him. He told me what he was going to do, and – I finished the job for him. If that was a crime, then I have committed a crime.'

Hooper could constrain himself no longer.

'We've got Madden so tight that he'll never get away,' he exulted. 'Let's go and talk to him.'

*   *   *

In the big, lovely room, the only room which retained the atmosphere of the Hall as it had been twenty years ago Colonel Madden was standing with his back to the fireplace, the fire half hidden by his bulk, and holding a brandy glass in both hands. His eyes looked veiny, his face very red and coarse, with the skin of a heavy drinker. He stared bull-like at Roger and the others as they came in. Lionel Foley was sitting on a couch, with one leg up, the ankle heavily bandaged, and the other leg hanging over the side. Kathleen Russell sat on a pouffe, as casual and at ease here as she was at her sister's home; the firelight shone on her auburn hair, making her glow with beauty. It was reflected in her eyes, too, and she was outwardly very calm.

Foley said sarcastically: 'All day and all night. Don't you coppers ever sleep?'

'Not on the job,' Roger answered brusquely. 'Colonel Madden, will you be good enough to answer a few questions?'

'Depends what they are?' croaked Madden.

'They concern the murder cases being investigated,' Roger said with deliberate formality. 'What time did you arrive at this house tonight?'

Madden hadn't been expecting that.

'Hour ago, I suppose.'

'Where had you been until then?'

'At my cottage. Where'd you think?'

'Were you alone at the cottage?'

'Always am, except in the mornings when the woman comes in. What's all this about?' Madden gave the impression that he would have liked to shout, but that his voice was too hoarse.

'Have you seen a stable lad named Tree, Frederick Tree, tonight?'

'Saw him this evening, at the Arncott Arms, I had some business to discuss with an acquaintance there.' The Colonel would always have an alibi for being in a pub; would he have one for Tree's murder? And for the barman's? 'What's all this about, West?'

'When did you last see Tree?'

'Must have been about eight o'clock, I suppose. Might have been earlier – not very sure. He went home. Why?'

'Does anyone have the key of your cottage, Colonel Madden?'

'Daresay,' said Madden. 'You've got one, haven't you, Martha? The daily woman's got one, too. Dozens of keys, who cares who has a key?'

Roger said: 'Were you associated with Tree in any way?'

Madden said: 'None of your business,' and glowered. 'We're both interested in horses and racing. Common interest, that's all.'

Roger didn't comment, and Hooper looked puzzled, as if he could not understand why Roger was delaying the charge.

Kathleen Russell hugged her knees, looked across at Lionel Foley with a faint smile, and said:

'There is such a lot of family loyalty and tradition in this house that I don't think you'll find out the truth this way, Mr West. But I'm not one of the family, and I've no interest in Colonel Madden's future. He was associated with Fred Tree. He's often told me that. Tree supplied him with much of the stable information, and Colonel Madden passed this on to the *Racecourse* and other magazines. I am the secretary to one of the directors of the company which owns the magazines.'

Lionel protested: 'Damn it, Kate!'

Lady Foley moved to a chair and sat down, as if this final revelation was too much for her.

'Is that true, Colonel Madden?' Roger asked.

Madden glared at the girl.

'He didn't give me any stable secrets, only information I could have picked up from local gossip, that's all.'

'As a matter of fact that isn't true,' stated Kathleen. 'I might be said to have a foot in each stable. I know that information which my brother-in-law didn't want to be known was often in the sporting papers, and it certainly didn't come from anybody else. My sister was aware of it, and also aware of your activities, Colonel Madden. Because of it, the Gale stable won a reputation for being slack, and consequently a lot of owners avoided it. The only thing that my sister got wrong was in thinking that Lady Foley and Lionel were involved in this, too. I think I've disabused her.'

Madden was still staring at her

'You little bitch,' he said, very distinctly. 'I've known you for fifteen years, and you'd let me down like this. You little—'

'That's enough,' Roger intervened sharply. 'What has made you talk so freely now, Miss Russell? Loyalty to your employers?'

'No,' Kathleen answered calmly. 'They don't know that I'm here this week-end. I came down to see my sister and brother-in-law because Lionel asked me to. Lionel wanted them to train his horse, Shoestring, on credit for a few months – if they wouldn't, he knew that he would have to sell it. I came down to help.'

'How well do you know Mr Foley?'

'Quite well,' announced Kathleen. 'As a client of my employer's bookmaking business, and also a little more intimately.' She turned and stretched out a hand, touching Lionel's. 'It's all right, darling, this had to come out sooner or later, and I think your mother can absorb it as well now as she ever will be able to. As a matter of fact I've come to have a very great respect for your mother, she has a lot more courage than I expected. It isn't true that the Foleys have run to seed.' The matter-of-factness of the girl was fascinating. 'We haven't let anyone know about our intention to get married because we knew you would disapprove, Lady Foley, and there was no point in making matters worse. If you'd been amenable about having Shoestring here, we would have waited until Shoestring was beginning to make money. We had a peculiar idea, you see, that if Lionel could prove that there was money in the horse, your objections would vanish. Were we very far wrong?'

Lady Foley said: 'In what other ways have you deceived me, Lionel?'

'Now, Mother—'

'Don't try to get up, darling,' Kathleen said, and jumped up, to press her hands against Lionel's shoulder. 'You won't help if you hurt your ankle any more. Lady Foley, you may not believe it, but the deception was simply to try to avoid hurting you. Lionel hated doing that.'

Colonel Madden growled deep in his throat: 'Martha, I wouldn't trust the trollop an inch further than I could see her. Why, when I first knew her—'

'When I was new at the office you used to take me out to the theatre and to expensive restaurants, because you wanted my help to get credit with the firm,' Kathleen said. 'But that's a long time ago, Colonel, and I don't owe you a thing. In fact I don't owe anybody a thing, as far as I know. That's a very satisfying way to live.'

'You've overlooked one debt,' Roger put in unexpectedly.

Kathleen looked surprised.

'What debt is that?'

Roger said: 'Your debt to the law.'

She glanced down at Lionel Foley.

'Must you talk in riddles, Mr West?'

'That's no riddle,' Roger said. 'Chief Inspector, will you stand by the couch and watch Mr Foley? Snell, cover the door, please. Lady Foley, I think you know the truth as well as I do.'

Hooper, on the move, was completely out of his depth. Percy Snell hovered about the door as if prepared to throw himself at anyone who attempted to reach it. Kathleen Russell was still standing behind young Foley, with her hands on his shoulders.

'What's on your mind?' Lionel demanded.

'Miss Russell's debt to the law,' Roger said. 'And yours,

Mr Foley. Miss Russell drove you from the Gale stables this evening, via the Arncott Arms. You had telephoned the barman who met you in the yard behind the inn, and whom you killed. I don't know whether Miss Russell knew that. I do know that she drove you to Colonel Madden's cottage this evening. She helped you to the cottage. You were both there when Tree entered, and you killed Tree between you. Then you left the cottage and came here, believing that Colonel Madden would be blamed for that murder, and for complicity in the others. Lady Foley, you knew that your son had committed the earlier crimes – killing the Cartwrights. You saw him driving that car. I imagine he took it over from two accomplices, with the body in it. You know that he buried the lad's body – he had to rid himself of it quickly. You knew that if the car were thoroughly searched it would reveal your son's bloodstained fingerprints. You preferred to condemn your brother to death, rather than your son. When it came to the test, you had too great a love for him.'

Lionel Foley was trying to get to his feet. Kathleen Russell had stopped pressing against his shoulders, and was staring at Roger as if she hated him. Madden gaped.

'You can't prove—' Kathleen began, but broke off, as if she realized the danger of what she had started to say.

Then Lionel Foley took the automatic out of his pocket.

CHAPTER XIX

SHOWDOWN

LADY FOLEY said in a sighing voice: 'Lionel,' and actually swayed, but she did not sit down. Kathleen did not seem to notice the gun. Colonel Madden said: 'Good God!' and backed against the mantelpiece.

'Put that gun down,' Hooper ordered. 'Don't try any funny stuff with us.'

'Killing myself won't exactly be funny,' Lionel said, 'but it looks as if it will be necessary. Want to come with me, Kate? I couldn't stand a trial and all the attendant unpleasantness, and my mother doesn't deserve that kind of mud either. I didn't think you'd ever lie to try to save me, Mother. Why did you? Do you think Uncle is more to blame than I for the mess I've made of my life?'

'Put that gun down,' Hooper ordered again.

'I shouldn't come any nearer,' Lionel advised, in a matter-of-fact voice. 'I've now killed three people on my own. Kate didn't kill Fred Tree, she didn't know why I was going to the pub or cottage either. My ankle's nothing like so bad as I made out, and I can move about all right. I got to the pub and fixed Sammy Links – the poor devil thought he had a bonus coming. I'd told Fred to go to the cottage in an emergency, and I knew all about the emergency after Mabel had been rescued! So I killed both men myself, and don't forget that. Like to know more? You coppers were so sure that I couldn't move about much that I slipped out of the back of the Gales' house without any trouble. Kate didn't even know! You'll never get Kate as an accessory, West, she didn't know a thing about it. Did you, Kate? But you might still prefer to come with me than live without me.'

Kathleen said: 'Lionel, you're lying. Tell me you're lying. You didn't kill—'

'The best lawyers would advise me to deny it, but it wouldn't do any good,' Lionel said, 'and as I've told you, I propose to save my dear mother the final indignity of a trial in the family. I shall bequeath her all my worldly possessions, one horse, namely Shoestring. *Don't come any nearer, Hooper.* It wouldn't make any difference to me if I had to kill you first.'

'You'd never have the guts to kill yourself,' Hooper sneered.

'Don't you believe it,' retorted Lionel. 'Like to know something, Mother? Horses may have got me into debt but they also got me out of it. I got the key to the Gale stables from Fred Tree. He left the bolts drawn for me. I went to kill Silver Monarch, of course. He was the one horse I was afraid Shoestring could never beat. Also, his owner was Corrison – and the Corrison Stable did more to ruin the Foleys than anyone else. Did you find that out, West?' Lionel did not wait for an answer, but went on: 'It was a pity that Ted Cartwright recognized me. I had to kill him, but – perhaps I've always had the capacity to kill. I can honestly say that it didn't worry me, except that it might put me into prison for life. I used two old friends of mine to work on Syd, who heard the noise of the Austin engine. My friends delivered Syd to me, because I had the car in among the trees. I was going to kill him there and bury him, but the horses were on the way back, and a police car was prowling. I had to get away quickly, so I took him to the garden– no one would be surprised to see the Austin there. He came round in the car, and threw his cap out to try to attract attention. I was sorry about Syd, but it was obviously his life or mine.'

He stopped, but no one said a word.

'These – er – friends,' he went on. 'They had to help, as I had a little hold over them. Remember when Taurus was attacked in his stable last year, and a jockey was killed saving his life? My friends did that job. I won't go into details about how I knew, but I knew – and they also knew that after old

Cartwright was killed they would hang – it was their second murder. We were all in it, sink or swim. I thought they'd make sure of Mabel, but I gather you were too much of a hero, West.'

Roger said: 'Just a policeman.'

'Damned scoundrel!' Madden rasped. 'My God, I've had to sail pretty close to the wind at times, but this beats the lot.'

Lady Foley sat motionless, staring at her son.

Kathleen looked down at him, too. He was sitting on the arm of the couch, and she was nearest him. He could see everyone, and keep them covered with the small automatic, which he held close to his body, as if afraid that someone would try to take it away from him.

'We had to fix Mabel,' Foley went on. 'That was the key point. If you'd started to question her about George Ansell you would have found out that her Fred sold information to me, and knew about the Taurus job last year. We didn't want you on to Fred, because we couldn't rely on him to keep quiet. Damned funny thing,' Lionel added, in a harder voice. 'I'd never seen myself as a murderer, but once I'd done the deed I didn't care how far I went so as to cover up. I thought I'd get by, as the dear Colonel and George Ansell were the obvious villains. I'd much rather watch dear Uncle swing than swing myself, and I don't think his trial would have worried my mother very much. It wouldn't be a bad idea if I put you away, Uncle, you're nothing but a drain on the family purse, and that's already slender enough. Like it as a dying favour, Mother?'

His mother raised her hands, and then began to move towards him. His eyes narrowed. He got off the couch and hopped back to the wall, so that no one could spring on him and take him by surprise. Hooper, nearest the couch, looked as if he would like to take a risk, but Roger raised a hand to him, and he stood very still.

Lady Foley said: 'Give me that gun, Lionel.'

'Now, Mother, don't be silly. I know exactly what I'm go-

ing to do, and how to do it. Don't imagine that it's all for the
sake of the old family name, either. I don't fancy months in
jail, or the court, or the condemned cell. I took a calculated
risk. One thing led to another; the barman was a look-out man
last night, so he had to go, and Tree – well, I've told you about
Tree. I did my damnedest, but I always knew that if I couldn't
get away with it, I'd have to kill myself. So don't try to stop
me.'

His mother went nearer, with her right hand held out.

'Give me that gun,' she said, in the same still voice.

'Mother—'

'For God's sake get away!' Madden cried.

'Lionel, if you don't—'

Then Roger waved his hand, and Hooper, Snell and Roger
moved at the same time. Lionel saw them, but his mother was
very close to him. He flung out his left arm, pushed her away,
and fired wildly towards Hooper. The Chief Inspector
winced, but the bullet which hit his shoulder did not stop him.
Next moment he had one of Lionel's arms and Snell had the
other. Roger had an arm round Lady Foley, protectingly,
while she stood staring at her son as if he carried hope away
with him.

Lionel said savagely: 'All right, I hope they put you in the
witness box, that ought to make you happy. I hope they make
you testify against me.'

The Colonel said: 'Martha, I'm terribly sorry, terribly. I
wish I could help, I wish I could tell you how sorry I am.'

Kathleen Russell did not say a word.

*   *   *

'I can't help it whether I'm believed or not,' Kathleen said,
at the police station an hour later. 'I did not know that Lionel
was the murderer. He persuaded me that it was Colonel Madden. He told me he wanted to go and place a bet at the pub,
and to go and see the Colonel at the cottage. As he couldn't
walk, I drove him. I didn't know that anyone else was in the

cottage. I was surprised to find the Colonel here when we arrived, but I didn't think anything of it.'

'Were you here on instructions from your employers?' Roger asked quietly.

'I was not.'

'Did your sister know or suspect that he was involved?'

'Daphne and John?' Kathleen said heavily. 'No, they didn't suspect him at all, they thought he was the one Foley who was quite reliable because of a genuine love of horses. And they really believed that Silver Monarch was killed in mistake for Shoestring. Mr West—'

'Yes?'

'Will you try to make it clear to them that I did not know?'

'I'll tell them the facts, as soon as they're all available,' Roger said flatly. 'You'll be seeing them before I do. We don't propose to detain you, you are at liberty to go. I believe that Mr Hooper has a car at your disposal. Mr Gale's car has already been returned.'

Kathleen stood up slowly; and it was the first time that he had seen her hesitate and in her way afraid. Soon, she would have to face her sister and her brother-in-law.

*　　　*　　　*

It was midnight.

Roger stifled a yawn, Percy Snell leaned back in a chair at the small desk, and rubbed his eyes. Hooper finished telephoning his Chief Constable, saying almost smugly: 'Yes, it's all sewn up, sir. We haven't got Foley's two accomplices yet, but we know their names and we'll soon pick them up. Clean sweep, sir, largely due to Superintendent West ... Yes, I'll tell him. Good night.' He put down the receiver, and forced a grin at Roger. 'The Chief wants to offer his congratulations.'

Roger grinned.

'You forgot to tell him that you were on the job, too.'

'Me?' Hooper sounded disgusted. 'If it had been left to me, I'd have Madden in the lock-up now, and young Foley would be laughing his head off. I think I could have made a case against Madden, too; don't see how he would have ducked it. The two swabs we haven't caught yet might have let the cat out of the bag, but I'm not so sure we would have caught them. No fingerprints on the car, according to the report, and – well, anyway, what made you plump for young Foley instead of the Colonel?'

'I'll tell you in the morning.'

'You'll tell me now. I've got to go home and report to my missus, and she won't be palmed off.' Hooper winked at Snell. 'Come on Handsome, let's have it.'

Roger said: 'I was pretty sure that Lady Foley had set fire to that car, and she certainly wouldn't have done it except for herself, her son or, just conceivably, for Colonel Madden. So one of the trio was involved. Young Foley didn't satisfy me with his story. His alibi for Ted's murder wasn't established. He was in debt. I could imagine him driving that car off and trying to wreck it and set fire to it for his own sake, and even conceivably for his mother – but the more I thought of such a sacrifice for his mother, the less I thought it likely. The affair started because of bad blood between them. That's existed for years, and I simply couldn't see young Foley as a self-sacrificing hero – so, he wanted that car destroyed for his own sake.'

'You knew as early as that?' marvelled Hooper.

'Not for certain, I simply had my eyes on him,' Roger said. 'I didn't know any more than you about George Ansell's part. I couldn't take any action until we had more of the facts available. I had one of my really bad moments when we discovered that Mabel Tree was missing.'

'You're telling me!'

'Know the truth about this job?' asked Snell unexpectedly. 'Didn't have enough time to think. That's what we coppers want – more time to think. This ought to have taken a week, three or four days at least, instead of which we didn't have even twenty-four hours. Who'd be a policeman?'

'Wouldn't be anything else,' said Hooper. Then he gave a gargantuan yawn. 'Better hit the hay, I suppose, it's all tied up now as far as it can be. Bet Lady F. won't get much sleep to-night. Kate Russell neither. Think she was as innocent as she made out? Wouldn't have been better to keep her here, would it?'

'If you mean, will she kill herself, I think she's the last person to attempt it,' Roger said. 'As for whether she knew — we haven't got enough to go on; we'll have to hand that question over to the legal chaps. Shouldn't think the Gales will be very happy about any of it,' Roger went on. 'Pity. I took to John Gale.'

'After this lot's blown over, he'll probably get on a lot better,' said Hooper. 'When it gets out that Fred Tree was the tout, working through Madden, owners will know that the main leakage has gone. He's a damned good trainer, never been any doubt about that — bit too soft when dealing with his lads, that's all. If he'd fired Tree a year ago, a lot of this might never have happened. Right?'

'Don't know,' answered Roger.

'Tell you one thing,' went on Hooper. 'One pair of so-and-so's will be happier after this is all over. I can't see Mabel Tree putting on widow's weeds for long, and I can't see George Ansell taking any more notice of his father's disapproval. Nice to know someone besides you drew some dividends.' He gave another huge yawn. 'Okay, let's get some shut-eye. I'll drop you at your hut as I go home.'

'Is that chap of yours who sent me round by the Cut still on duty?'

'Bound to be.'

'Let's find him, I'd like to tell him that it was one of his red-letter nights.'

'No wonder you're such a damned good copper,' Hooper said. 'Okay.'

*　　　*　　　*

Roger was back at the Yard the following afternoon, and at home the following evening. His two sons, Martin called Scoopy and Richard sometimes called Fish, had newspapers spread out in the kitchen, and were eagerly searching for references to him. Richard, aged thirteen, was the first to say:

'Did you get any tips, Dad?'

'Don't be a clot,' Scoopy said promptly. 'He didn't have time, and in any case it's no use following tips on horses, is it, Dad?'

'I think I have a Lady Foley attitude towards racehorses,' Janet West said, from the gas stove. 'If you boys want any supper tonight, you'd better get those newspapers off the table, and put the cloth on.'

'I'm famished,' Roger announced.

'Did you?' asked Richard.

'Did I what?'

'Get any tips?'

Roger grinned. 'You don't get any better, do you, Fish? No, I didn't get any tips – but in spite of your mother, you've my permission to put a shilling each way on Shoestring any time you want to.'

'What's each way?' inquired Richard, deeply interested.

'Shilling to win, and shilling for a place, that's second or third,' explained Scoopy scornfully. 'If you don't know that, what's the use of thinking about betting?'

'I'd just back a horse to win,' Richard said. 'Shoestring, did you say?'

Four months later, when the trial of Lionel Foley was over, and he had been hanged; and when the trial of his two accomplices was over, and they had been sentenced to life imprisonment; and when Hooper had told Roger that the Gales seemed to be doing better; and when Kathleen Russell had given up her London job, and was on her way to Australia, to live, Roger found his younger son studying the back page of a newspaper very intently. It was a Saturday morning. He did not speak, just watched the boy, who rubbed one of his rather prominent ears, and then looked up.

'Dad?'

'Yes?'

'Shoestring is going to be in a race today.'

'Really?' Roger was taken by surprise. 'I didn't know — what are the odds?'

'Apparently you can get ten to one,' announced Richard carefully. 'There's a boy at school whose father does a lot of betting, and I've been getting some inside dope. Would you mind awfully if I put half a crown on him, to win? You did agree up to a shilling.'

'Have you got half a crown?'

'Oh, yes.'

'Then do what you like with it,' said Roger, and looked up as Scoopy, massive and tall for his fourteen years, came in from the garden, hands dirty from cleaning his bicycle.

'I say, Dad!'

'Yes, Scoop.'

'Did you know that horse, Shoestring, is running today?'

'I know that you two will get in trouble if you sound so professional about horse-racing,' Roger said. 'Richard's just told me.'

'Would you mind if I put two shillings each way on it?'

'That'll cost you four shillings,' Roger said.

'Only if it doesn't get a place.'

Roger grinned. 'Right. Who's your bookmaker?'

'Oh, there's this fellow at school,' Scoopy said, and winked at Richard; it was obvious that they had conspired together to get his permission, and so to bypass their mother, who was upstairs.

Roger was late getting to the office. When he arrived, a little after ten o'clock, he found Percy Snell waiting for him.

'I know,' Roger said. 'Shoestring is running today.'

'First time out,' announced Snell, 'and I've had a word with Hooper, who'd had a word with Gale, who says it can't lose.

Ten to one, too. Damned funny thing if Lady Foley was to have a winner, wouldn't it? I always thought she'd sell that horse, but—'

'Put me a pound each way,' Roger said.

'Blimey, you're breaking the bank. Okay. But if I were you I'd make it a fiver.'

'I can't afford to lose ten quid,' Roger said.

'Be a devil,' Snell urged. 'I won't tell Janet.'

Roger said: 'Well, I haven't put a penny on a horse since last year's Derby, so I'll take a chance.'

He was home, with the television switched on, and the blinds drawn in the living-room, at 3 o'clock that afternoon. The boys, usually out playing cricket, had mysteriously cried off. The horses were lining up for the three o'clock at Newbury.

Roger heard footsteps, and turned round to see Janet in the doorway.

The commentator kept talking, until suddenly he exclaimed: 'They're off.'

'*They're off!*' echoed Richard.

'There's Shoestring, in the Foley colours – won't it be wonderful when we have *coloured* television,' Scoopy said.

'Quiet!' ordered Janet.

Roger glanced at her sharply.

'He's fourth,' Richard said tensely. 'A horse often runs up from fourth position to first, that chap at school told me.'

'He's third,' breathed Martin.

'Good Lord!' thought Roger. 'He's going to win, he's catching up – he's even second!'

'Go on, Shoestring!' Janet cried. 'Go on, you'll do it, you'll do it!'

'*Shoestring!*' roared Richard and Scoopy.

'Darling! He's there, he's won, he's first past the post,' cried Janet. Her eyes were glowing and she was almost dancing with delight. 'I didn't tell you but I put ten shillings on it to win – the milkman took the bet for me. That's five *pounds* I've won.'

'You little hypocrite,' Roger said, and then squeezed her arm.

The boys were pummelling each other in delight, and the commentator was saying what a remarkable race the jockey had ridden on Shoestring, the *twenty*-to-one outsider. Then the picture changed, and Roger saw Lady Foley patting Shoestring's nose as his saddle was being taken off.

*   *   *

'It's a queer kind of courage,' Roger said to Janet, later, 'but it's courage all right. I wonder what is going through her mind?'

For regular early information about forthcoming novels, send a postcard giving your name and address in block capitals to Mrs. Jean Povey, Hodder and Stoughton Limited, St. Paul's House, Warwick Lane, London, EC4P 4AH.

CRIME AND DETECTION FROM CORONET

BY JOHN CREASEY

Gideon Series

☐ 18803 0	Gideon's Men	35p
☐ 14822 5	Gideon's Staff	35p
☐ 15043 2	Gideon's Risk	35p
☐ 00868 7	Gideon's Fire	35p

The Toff Series

☐ 18624 0	The Toff And The Runaway Bride	30p
☐ 02415 1	The Toff On Fire	30p
☐ 00795 8	Follow The Toff	35p

The Baron Series

☐ 15113 7	Nest Egg For The Baron	25p
☐ 02486 0	The Baron Goes Fast	30p
☐ 18306 3	Black For The Baron	30p
☐ 18305 5	Sport For The Baron	30p
☐ 18763 8	The Baron And The Arrogant Artist	35p

Inspector West Series

☐ 17846 9	Murder London—New York	35p

All these books are available at your bookshop or newsagent, or can be ordered direct from the publisher. Just tick the titles you want and fill in the form below

CORONET BOOKS, P.O. Box 11, Falmouth, Cornwall.

Please send cheque or postal order. No currency, and allow the following for postage and packing:

1 book—10p, 2 books—15p, 3 books—20p, 4–5 books—25p, 6–9 books—4p per copy, 10–15 books—2½p per copy, 16–30 books—2p per copy, over 30 books free within the U.K.

Overseas—please allow 10p for first book and 5p per copy for each additional book.

Name...

Address..

....